# WELL UP FOR IT!

# WELL UP FOR IT!

**Simon Cheetham and Carl Eldridge**

**HEAD-HUNTER BOOKS**

First published in October 2005 by Head-Hunter Books

PO Box 26066

Copyright © 2005 Simon Cheetham and Carl Eldridge

Head-Hunter Books

ISBN 0-9548542-4-1

Printed in Great Britain by

MPG Books Limited, Bodmin

# Foreword

I'VE been watching Chelsea since I was a five-year-old. A hotdog and a place on the Shed, cheering on the likes of Peter Osgood, rain or shine. Then it hit me. The bond. Week in week out I was with people who were just like me; who loved Chelsea and hated everyone else. And get this: they hated us too. I grew to appreciate that more often than not, the action off the pitch was a lot more exciting than on it. Following Chelsea in those days opened up a whole new world for me. A world brimming with violence. Violence towards other fans. Those were, some would say, the halcyon days of football hooliganism. And I watched the rucks, rows and riots unfold before my very eyes. From Villa to Venezuela (pre-season tour 1977), I thought I'd seen it all: mean mobs, nutty turn-outs, king growlers, top boys, blade merchants, morris dancers, the lot. The fiercest fighting men ever to attend football matches in mainland Britain. I knew them; and they knew me. I saw them all as I followed my beloved Blues home and away. Or, at least I thought I knew them all, thought I'd seen 'em all. But that was before I read Well Up For It!

As I write this foreword for this extraordinary literary masterpiece, my hand trembles over the keyboard. I'm not a man who is used to fear: it's a stranger in my house. And I don't like strangers. Well, not in my house anyway. But as I battle to steady my fingers and press on, I find fear gripping me. A fear that I never knew existed. Total fear. Frighteningly etching itself over my face as I write. Look at me for God's sake...I am a wreck! And the reason? Oh, that's easy mate. The reason is I have just read the most harrowing accounts of top level football violence ever recorded. I'm no grass. I'm not a snitch. And I very rarely cheat at cards. Me and the OB? We've got an understanding. I tell 'em nothing. That's what they expect. Or did, until I sent them a copy of this book. Because if the authorities don't take action, immediate action having read the chilling chapters that lay before you, dear reader, humanity hasn't a hope. Something must be done. Think of the children. As God is my witness, I renounce all violence to all men...just do something to rid this evil from our land.

Martin King
Base Camp, Mount Everest
October 2005

# Contents

# Nonces, ponces, plums and plod

RIGHT. First things first.

The very fact you've picked up this book means you're a lad. Top lad maybe. You are probably a dresser. A boy. A sort. You love the buzz, the whiz, the action.

You're loyal. Loyal to your team. You're loyal to your mates. You're loyal to your country.

You like to look good – no law against that – least not when I last looked.

You spend all week looking forward to the weekend. You put up with the mundane, day-to-day shit because you know come Saturday the real fun starts.

That's the day when you and your mates travel to some pony, one-eyed hick town in the smelly North to watch your team. Before, during and after the match there's the little matter of having it with the home fans, the OB and whoever else is out there looking for a pasting.

Not every Saturday, obviously, because sometimes you're at home.

Or maybe you're just a scarfer trying to give it the big one. Look round at the other people in the shop. They know you're a scarfer. It's written all over your face. Put the book down and go and buy a copy of Four-Four-Two and get all excited at the "in-depth Q & A with Bolton's Jay-Jay Okocha".

Thinking about it, maybe you're a plum, a complete muppet giving it large. Or perhaps you're a nonce.

If you ARE a nonce, put the fucking book down NOW and take yourself down the nick to sign the sex offenders' register.

Or perhaps you're OB. If you ARE OB, put the fucking book DOWN and leave the shop.

Go and spend your time chasing criminals who beat up old ladies, or stop all the illegal refugees getting into our country, OK?

Anyway, you get there, come out of the station and they're waiting: The Welcome Committee. A couple of dozen lads dressed in what they call fashion. It's laughable. They're a joke. A complete fucking joke.

They look as if they've just come in from the fields pulling fucking sugar beet from the soil. Adidas Rio trainers, I ask you – in 2005!

But you're not worried. OK, there are only eight or so of you lot. You're outnumbered, what, three to one? But those odds are OK, more than OK.

One of the herberts outside the station shouts "They're here!"

"We're here alright," you think. "And pretty soon they'll wish we weren't." You notice a couple of their mob bouncing up and down, giving it the Big I Am. You just carry on, out of the station. Your eyes quickly take everything in. Watching to see when their boys make their move.

You stick together. No one has said a word since you left the station. No one has to. You've done this a hundred times before. Possibly thousands. Not millions though. That'd be exaggerating.

In Preston, Plymouth, Portsmouth and Poole (pre-season friendly) the routine has been the same.

Suddenly, one of their lads makes his move. Their numero uno, their guv'nor, their main boy. He's just a few feet away now, you can see his eyes. They're full. Full of hate. Is he wearing mascara? Must be the fucking street lights.

And so it begins. The rumble, the off, the ag, the how's your father, the knuckle, the grunt. The very reason you're there. The reason you're all mates, the reason you follow your team.

The reason you live and breathe. Nothing can compare with this. You can keep drugs, sex, booze. Keep them all. Keep them all and shove them up your arse. Sideways.

These people who go on TV and write in the papers and tell us all that they don't understand football hooligans make you laugh. Course they don't understand.

Let them go back to their poncey middle class dinner parties and their posh restaurants. Their Saturday afternoons are spent in garden centres or fucking Ikea. They have never tasted what you taste every week: The buzz.

So this book's for you. Some of the stories, well, you'll recognise them.

Why? I'll tell you why.

Because like me and my firm, you'll have had the same experiences, the same rucks, the same rows.

Like you, I've read a load of hoolie books, some good, some not so good.

But I've never read one that gets under the skin of a firm. One that gives it to you straight.

That's what this book's about. The good days and the bad. And oh yes, there have been some bad!

Enjoy.

# CHAPTER ONE

# Passport to paradise

THE summer. Long hot days, birds walking about with next to nothing on. Just showing you enough of a thong or a Chinese tattoo on their arse to get you interested.

Just back from Kos, Ibiza or some other Med fleshpot with an all-over tan, lovebites and a vague memory of some clown from Stoke who got lucky at 4am and hit the jackpot. All the poor cow's got now is a huge credit card bill, sunburn and a nagging feeling that the Happy Potter may well have left a calling card, either a dose of something or perhaps a little souvenir that will arrive next Spring. Not that it's too much of a problem. Back down the clinic and another 300 notes on the flexible friend will soon sort that out. Won't be the first time.

They say Italian women soon go to seed. Well, they, whoever "they" are, obviously have never tipped up around this place. These birds, by the time they're mid-twenties are spent. Finished. They've already had the thick end of a decade of what passes for life around here. They've been shagged, slapped, drugged, let down, pissed on (probably both literally and metaphorically), battered and beaten. They've hooked up with more losers than a bent jockey, but fair play to them they keep coming back for more.

They've been married, separated, divorced, remarried, co-habitated and gone back to Mum. They've tried life with criminals, low-life, older men, younger lads, Yardies and yes-men. They've had twins, triplets and terminations. They've sat at home while their men are inside, in court, on a boozy ferry to some England game in a far-flung field, in the pub, in bed with another sort or just plain gone missing.

They've worked at every checkout at every soulless supermarket in town. The height of their working lives was when the minimum wage came in, that's because their money went up.

They're 25 but look nearly twice that. They've been on 40-a-day for years, and now they're on a couple of bottles of cheap vodka too, just to get them through.

Their little daughter is 10 going on 25, and so the scene continues with the next generation making the same mistakes as this one.

For the women, that's it. There's no escape. They're in it for the long haul. Once they've past their sell-by date the blokes round here have moved on to the younger birds. That was your youth that was, girl. Enjoy it?

For the geezers it's different. Fuck me, nothing's changed round here since Stone Age times. You know, when Leeds had a decent side. The women stay at home, and the blokes go out. End of story.

Hunting and gathering it was called then. Going out for a row it's called now. You see if the women are bored to fuck, well, that's just hard luck, love. They've got kids to get to school, shopping, washing and their bloke's dinner to put on the table. "Somewhat shackled by the pressures of modern living", I've heard it described by some bird on Woman's Hour. Has a bit of a ring to it.

For blokes like you and me, we have a passport out...football. Yeah, occasionally there'll be a stroppy bird, who starts to put her foot down. You know the kind. Some Daddy's girl ball-breaker who doesn't see why she should do all the work while her bloke is out five nights a week and every Saturday with his mates. Pissing the hard-earned up the wall or handing over serious dough to the travel agent for those European games, whilst she and the kids are walking round in last year's clobber from the market.

This is when a geezer has to take quick and serious action. It's bad enough being dissed in front of your mates by your skirt, but if you're seen to cave in and actually take any notice of the bint, that's it, you're done, mate. Might as well join the knitting circle or go the whole hog and have your bollocks snipped and become a lady-boy. Fair play, once these birds cotton on to the way things are done, more often than not they're as good as gold.

Anyway, where was I? Oh yeah, football. Well, that's what this book is about really, football. The beautiful game. You believe all that do you?

The beautiful game, the working man's ballet? Sounds great, doesn't it? Almost cultural. Not so cultural when there's a couple of dozen Scousers a few steps behind you ready to practice a bit of DIY surgery on you with their good friend Stanley. Or when Milan's finest Carabanierri backed up by a mob of mental Inter fans are very keen to give you a warm Italian welcome. But, you get out of it, you always do. You may pick up a few slaps or sometimes something a bit more serious, but a couple of nights later you're back in the boozer telling everyone who wants to know what went on last Saturday, and making plans for the next sortie.

I've read all this bollocks about us being an "Island Race", having all this violence and frustration in our genes. You know, we just HAVE to invade foreign lands and have it with the dagos or we'll all go ga-ga. Maybe something in that. But then again, Malta's a fucking island and they don't seem so keen on jumping in a speedboat and giving it to the Italians or whoever. I have to say I do enjoy watching these intellectual pricks getting their knickers in a twist about football hooliganism. There was that Scouse character with the regulation Mersey 'tache a few years back who cropped up on the TV every time there'd been an off, and explained to everyone that it was because we'd all been dropped on our heads as babies or because we'd never been breast fed. The cheeky git even got some dough from the government to open some football research unit.

Then you get the ex-lads. You know the kind, they're now well into their 40s, no hair to speak off, just a fucking huge beer belly and a long forgotten grade D in their English O-Level. Fuck me, they're now a novelist and social commentator on all things hoolie. That's when lads like you and me think we're well into the first stages of Alzheimers. These characters start to re-write history, just to make themselves more credible. We're now told that Sheffield United brought 500 to that League Cup tie back in '89 and they dished out so much knuckle, we were begging them to stop and their top boy, the creator of this fine piece of literature, ran our mob all over town, shagged all our women and was voted Mayor...all on that one night. And these books are not found next to the Brothers Grimm stuff, they're being sold in the fact section. Fancy that. Jesus, these books are everywhere. It's become a whole industry, and it does make me laugh to hear them all scratching each other's eyes out as they squabble over who's really written the biggest load of fiction since JK Rowling's last effort.

And now with the internet you have the "real" hoolie websites for those "in the know". Pictures of a bunch of spotty geeks marching up and down Shrewsbury High Street with their arms held out and their faces all pixelated out for security. Old codgers, who during their lunch hour at the building society, go under the names of "Shed Suicide Squad" or "England 4 Ever" and reminisce about ancient tear-ups back when Roy Wood's Wizzard were on Top of The Pops and we were all still getting used to decimal currency. All that material flapping about as their flared trousers were caught in the breeze.

And then there are the OB. John Peel once said about The Fall, that they were "always different, yet always the same". And so is the case with the police. One day, they've got it all sussed. Football hooliganism has been "eradicated". Then there's a fucking massive tear-up, and all of a sudden we're all going to hell in a handcart. Lads' front doors are being kicked in at 5am, and Operation "ArseWipe" is launched. Although, to be fair things have changed a lot over the past ten years. CCTV cameras have made it very difficult to get anything going in or anywhere near the ground. Although our mob did beat the system when we all turned up at Maine Road a couple of years back in masks of the London Philarmonic Orchestra. We took the Kippax, took liberties down Curry Mile, and got back to Piccadilly to read that night's performance of Carmen at the Royal Opera House had been cancelled as the string and woodwind sections of the LPO had all been nicked. Hence, with the help of mobile phones, firms intent on getting something together have an off miles away from the stadium. Only last season the Forest and Brighton lads took this to a new extreme when they all booked into Centre Parcs in Cheshire for a weekend to sort out their differences. £89 each for a two-berth chalet on a B&B basis. Pretty decent deal that, might mention it to my crew.

Anyway, don't let me keep you. You've just forked out for this book, you'll want to get to the meat, the real stuff. So, go on then fella. Get stuck in.

And who knows, on a rain-swept train station in Warsaw, or a smelly police cell in Sardinia. Or maybe a knocking shop in Copenhagen or a chippy in Sunderland, we may bump into each other. If you hear one of my mob shout, "Hey Aqua, that nonce is eyeballing you", just tell me you're "Well Up For It".

# CHAPTER TWO

# Battering Blackburn in BHS

SITTING in the garden of your local boozer necking bottles of Stella, smoking a bit of gear, maybe dropping a couple of Es. Lines of Charlie in the bogs.

Listening to the latest releases. You know, Ocean Colour Scene, Paul Weller (the guv'nor), Oasis.

Paradise. Or is it?

To the average muppet, perhaps it is. Gives them the chance to give it the big one. Put a few beers away and relive their youth. Talk bollocks with mates who are talking bollocks. They all know it's shite but they go on. They've got nothing else. They feel the need to get away from their fucking computer and their poxy office for a few hours; remind their birds just why they married them in the first place.

These geezers make me laugh.

They'll be there, dressed in God's know what – some shit stuff their wives bought them in M&S, or fake S.I. they've bought off eBay. Standing at the bar telling anyone in earshot what it was like in their day. Like some fucking war veteran who can't seem to see beyond life in the service.

How their music was the best; how their clothes were the dog's bollocks, how when they followed their team, their firm was number one.

I just smile, stub a Marlboro out with a Patrick Cox loafer and order another cold one. You see I know the score. They know I know the score. I know they know I know the score. That's the way I like it. It's called respect. I've done my bit. Big fucking bit at that. No one can take that away from me. They can try. Big mistake. I'm a face, a top boy, a main geezer. I have served my time. I've led our lot into battle in Birmingham. I've chased firms from Aberdeen to Aberystwyth. Other top boys know me, know my rep. And so they should. I've taken beatings, broken bones and been carved up. Pepper spray, CS gas, truncheons, blades, balloons filled with piss and a cushion cover filled with women's high-heeled shoes – fucking Service Crew? Muppets. I've used and been abused by the lot.

But I'm getting ahead of myself dear reader. Let me introduce myself, my name is Aqua. OK, I admit it – I wasn't christened Aqua! No, Mum and Dad chose Julian.

Nothing wrong with that now is there? A few spoons have felt the need to give me their thoughts on the selection over the years.

They've given it the big one, then wished they hadn't I can assure you.

So I'm Aqua. Think Aquascutum. I was dripping in the stuff when I got that mantle. Head to toe. Now the chavs have ruined all that. Or is that Burberry? Bit of both, maybe.

Anyway, I suppose I'd better give you the story so far, so here it is.

Like millions of other white working class kids, I grew up on a housing estate in a faceless home counties town. I can't say it was the roughest place on earth, because it wasn't. Yeah, you had to look after yourself otherwise you'd end up being taken for a plum. Sure, I had a few run-ins with other lads and the OB. But the violence wasn't the problem. I'll tell you what the real killer was and still is on these estates. Boredom.

Youth club? You must be having a laugh. I'm not one for table-tennis and mini snooker, all organised by some child-molesting freak in a beige anorak.

Boy's Brigade? Blue just ain't my colour. Cubs? Scouts? What? Spend the night in a poxy tent in the pissing rain with a load of mummy's boys who get their rocks off by washing some geezers car for 5p. Not for me.

No. There was just one thing that made sense. Football.

First of all playing, all day, every day. Two-a-side, eleven-a-side, thirty-fucking-three-a-side – it didn't matter.

We'd play in the street, in gardens, in parks, on the deck of The Mary Rose. On grass, tarmac, concrete, on some kind of man-made flooring material that they use in the space shuttle. Anywhere.

In rain, snow, hale – if there'd been a plague of locusts or if the local tip had erupted a la Etna, we'd have got stuck in regardless.

We didn't play for a team, as such. It was just a collection of the local lads my age, who wanted a kickabout and to have a laugh. We weren't interested in being part of an organised club where some do-gooding kiddy-fiddler with a second-hand manager's coat, a clipboard and a few plastic cones fancied themselves as the new Brian Clough, and none of us were kidding ourselves that we were about to be signed up by Liverpool. Most of us were already on 20-a-day and as much cider as we could get our hands on. And any-way, the local probation officers would probably have had some-thing to say about their charges being whisked off to Anfield on five-year contracts.

They say a professional player has a short career – well, not as short as the lads from my estate. As we grew up, other things began to come into the mix. Football was still the major influence in our lives, but along with the game came booze, birds, drugs, shop-lift-ing, glue-sniffing, TWOCing, setting fire to bus shelters and daubing inappropriate and offensive graffiti in white paint on walls and rail-way bridges.

Then the day came to go to my first professional game. Steve, my older brother, under a bit of pressure from Mum and Dad, caved in and grudgingly agreed to let me, the kid, join him and his merry band of lunatics. One of his regular mates wasn't about, so there was a spare space in the motor. Big brother wasn't over pleased, and the night before the game, I was briefed on my behaviour for the next day. I was not to "piss about, speak unless spoken to, embarrass me in front of the lads" and perhaps most important of all, "tell Mum and Dad what goes on at football".

Suddenly, everything made sense. The noise, the crowd, the smell. And that's just in the car going to the match. Steve's mates, Big Doug, Swanny and the legendary Short Trousered Dave – who, for a bet wore short trousers the whole of 1975 and liked it so much, that he continued, I believe to the present day.

My presence in the car was a novelty, and gave Steve's other passengers plenty of ammunition for ripping the piss out of him. He took some terrible stick as he drove to the ground, but fair play to him, he took all the flak on the chin – never once letting the lads get the better of him.

I still remember my first game, so vividly. Blackburn at home in the old second division – around 1980. I'd been preparing for the game all week. Reading about Blackburn's squad, who was going to play, who I should look out for on the pitch. We had been relegated a couple of years earlier, and were hopefully on the way back to the big time. For me, it was tactics, who was playing right-back and would our latest big signing find the back of the net. I was a walking Rothmans Football Yearbook. If any of my brother's mates wanted to know Port Vale's nickname, Millwall's record attendance or the Celtic line-up that won the 1967 European Cup – they only had to ask. They didn't.

On the way to the ground, the talk wasn't of how the team was doing, it was of events off the pitch. United had played away at Norwich the week before, picked up a useful 1-1 draw, and I was expecting to hear how the team had fared. But the conversation was all about "steaming in to the home end" and "putting carrot crunchers on their arses". I was decked out in a couple of scarves and half a dozen enamel badges, all declaring my dedicated love of United. Not one of my fellow supporters wore anything showing that they were football fans. Instead, they were dressed a bit like golf caddies – all pastel Pringle jumpers and training shoes. I'd noticed my brother's taste in clothing had changed quite a bit over the last few months, and his mates had gone down the same route. A few years back, when Steve had first started following United, it had been Dr Marten boots and Levis. Now it was tight designer jeans and wedge haircuts. I was only a kid, but even I thought they looked like a bunch of hairdressers. Didn't tell them though.

As with most football fans, Steve and his mates were creatures of habit. Always parked in the same spot, went to the same pub, bought a programme from their favourite seller.

And so it was that day.

I was ushered towards a table in the corner of The Railway Tavern, behind a fruit machine, well out of the prying eye of the landlord, a coke and a bag of cheese and onion crisps were thrust into my hand. I'd been in a few pubs before with Mum and Dad, on holiday, at Christmas or on a Sunday lunchtime. Then I'd sat quietly with an aunt or uncle, the ticking of the pub clock the main source of noise, the landlord's cat the topic of conversation.

But this was different. The bar looked like Fagan's kitchen. There was so much smoke I could only just see across the place and the juke box was cranked up to ear-splitting volume rattling out punk and rock tracks so distorted it was difficult to know if this was a record playing or a jet taking off from Heathrow.

It was clear that brother Steve and his mates were well known, and as we settled down around the table, there was a constant stream of visitors to our corner of the pub.

Handshakes and backslaps were exchanged, then reports of past games and previous trips were discussed. But, again, the performance of the team did not seem to be the on the agenda. As I munched my way through my crisps I listened to the exploits of Steve's friends.

John The Bus, a small ferret-looking character who, unsurprisingly worked for London Transport had been nicked at Norwich the week before. Vague Dave thought he was going to the cup game up at Burnley in a couple of weeks, but wasn't sure. Phil The Liar had gone to Carrow Road on his own, had a row with nine Norwich fans and put them all in hospital, fought with the OB until the police held up their hands, surrendered, and let him sit on the United bench. He then came on for the last couple of minutes and hit the bar. Forgetful Kev didn't show.

To make me feel a part of this crowd, one of Steve's mates came back from the bar with a bottle of Holsten Pils for me. "Get that down you little man," he said.

Just as I was looking forward to a second beer, a young lad, a United spotter, only a couple of years older than me rushed into the pub and over to our table. "They're here. Only about a dozen. They're looking in the window of British Home Stores – one of them is thinking of buying a duffel coat," he said.

With that, glasses were quickly drained and cigarettes hastily either lit or stubbed out.

Steve whispered to me: "Stay with me, OK?" Try to get rid of me I thought. This is brilliant!

A mob of about 20 of us snaked out of the pub, quickly yet slowly if you know what I mean. Obviously, no one wanted to draw any attention. Outside of The Railway, the young kid pointed up the street, "Bill's still with them – he'll let you know more when you get there, good luck lads." Steve took control of the situation, "Right let's get into BHS right away, split into four groups – see you up there."

Off we went, moving quickly, some of the lads already bouncing up and down – indulging in what's called "Pavement Dancing" – no-one talking just intent on getting to the department store. And there it was, BHS. Another young lad, obviously Bill, appeared as from nowhere. "They're up on level 2 in the electrical department. The big geezer's bought his duffel coat –£8.60 – and now one of them is looking at an angle-poised lamp for his study. He and his bird have just converted their garage into an office and..."

"Fuck me Bill, OK," said Steve.

In we went, me keeping close to Steve. Some of the lads went up on the escalator some used the lift. And there we were, in the electrical and home entertainment department. The Blackburn lads were gathered around the cash desk completing the transaction for the lamp, destined for a newly created northern office-cum-study.

One of their mob, taking a look at a washing machine clocked us, and suddenly we didn't have surprise on our side. "We are Rovers, We are Rovers," they sang – that was the signal, and Steve and his pals were on them. Everything seemed to happen in slow motion – the Rovers fans didn't have a chance as they were sent spinning into dish-washers and other white goods. The fracas spilt into the home furnishings section, and I saw Steve give a couple of Blackburn lads a terrible doing over a chaise longue.

I was a spectator, on the periphery – watching it all, taking it all in. I could feel the adrenaline pulsing though my veins, my heart beating like a drum. Suddenly, from nowhere a huge Rovers lad, leapt in front of me.

"Hold on to my angle-poised lamp, son – be a good lad," and he thrust the newly purchased item into my hands, then turned his back ready to return to the fray. What happened next, Steve reckoned later, was pure instinct. The same way great goalscorers such as Jimmy Greaves and Ian Wright could never really explain how they were at the right place at the right time to poach all those goals. Just as the Rovers lad turned I brought the lamp crashing down across the back of his head and he fell over a settee onto a nest of corner tables. As he laid there, eyes glazed, he turned his head to me – his face a picture of confusion and surprise.

Every bloke remembers their first bird, their first car, the first time they went to a Gilbert & Sullivan operetta – and so I'll never forget that Blackburn lad. He was Aqua's first victim.

If you're reading this mate, nothing personal, OK? If you let my publisher have your name and address, I'll get a cheque off to you right away for a new lamp.

It was then that everything changed for me. We made a quick exit from the store, split up again, meeting up on the home terrace just as the teams ran out.

I was surrounded by the older lads, all of them patting me on the back and shaking my hand.

"Fuck me Steve, there's one off the old block."

And so to the game. 1-1 it was, can't remember who scored for us, but we nearly had a pop at some Blackburn on the way back to the car. Northern nonces. Week after it was Palace away. Those Croydon toss-pots had it coming.

Now I had football. And precious little else.

School was a joke. Our teachers were nonces and plums. Some were planks. It was all they could do to keep the lid on the place, stop it all kicking off big time in RE. It was a laugh, when I bothered to turn up.

I was born in 1968 – the Swinging Sixties – in fact I was the product of the Summer of Love. Maybe Mum and Dad got high listening to Hendrix and Jefferson Airplane, then decided to walk naked into a meadow and make passionate love amongst the wild flowers. Yeah, maybe. Or perhaps Dad came back from The Labour Club after eight pints and a few shorts then double saveloy and chips, woke up my poor old Mum, had his wicked way before passing out with his socks still on. See, I can paint pictures with words.

My school years were the 70s and early 80s. All of our teachers seemed to have been trained in some secret socialist training college, maybe in Minsk, Bucharest or Yarmouth – somewhere out East anyway. They all had beards, wore crusty old tweed jackets with leather patches on the elbows and smoked pipes. And that was just the women. Yeah, ha ha. They were all (deep breath) against the bomb, pro-gay, anti-Thatcher, for a united Ireland, against nuclear power, they wanted to save the whale, introduce Rastafarian literature, Romanian drama and Albanian folk dancing to our curriculum.

They'd go on marches and demos supporting the miners, the trawler men and the man who says "Mind The Gap" at Embankment underground station. They'd arrange petitions to be sent to the South African government, the Metropolitan Police and the United Nations. They'd raise money for Sinn Fein, Green Peace, ETA – any fucking organisation on the planet who wanted to tear our country apart, put our Royal Family in a cell and send lads like me to a labour camp.

Oh, and in the few hours a week they had free, they'd try to teach me and my mates.

One in particular, Mr Ball – "Boys, call me Chaz, yeah?" – actually, mate, if it's all the same to you we'll call you Old Bollocks, OK?

– saw that we were just what he was looking for. He saw us as young impressionable working class lads, ripe for a spot of brainwashing – the latest generation of young Marxists ready to man the barricades and storm the winter palace. Old Bollocks saw us as a blank canvas, all ready and willing to join him in his Utopian dream. He "understood us", he "realised our frustrations and anger", Old Bollocks wanted to "release us from our working class repressed ideals" and "help us to understand and appreciate Italian Opera, Irish playwrights, Czech ballet and Japanese Haikus".

"Joolz," he'd say – I fucking hated being called fucking Joolz – "Joolz, man, why all that anger and aggression?" He'd tell me I was wallowing in my own self-imposed proletariat pit of self-pity. Oh really. "Joolz, man, you're a bright kid. Free your mind, knuckle down here at school, get some qualifications – go to uni Joolz, in five years you could be me."

Fuck me, the prick meant it.

I found a school report from my last year at school. I haven't got the time or inclination to list it all here – but let's just say no one really expected much from me. Even Old Bollocks gave up on me, and then he went off to teach at some public school in Dorset for five times his salary. Perhaps Old Bollocks wasn't as full as shit as I first thought.

Last I heard of him he was the Tory MP for some safe Conservative seat. He crops up on TV now and again banging on about hanging gays and sending black lads back to Africa.

So much for the great Marxist Revolution.

So, that was school. Sorry if you were expecting an in-depth list if all my degrees and exam passes! No. Stuff like that was for muppets.

Those plums went off to university and college, sponging off the state, sitting around smoking pot and listening to shit music for four years, then sitting in some office until they got a poxy gold watch then popped their clogs. End of story. That, my friend, was not for me.

When my mates and I left school, it was no big deal. After all, since we were 14 or so, hardly any of us had been there for more than a few days each term.

The teachers, apart from Old Bollocks, didn't bother with the likes of us. Why should they? My destiny was already planned. I was factory fodder.

In our town, boys like me have three choices.

The Ford factory, the bee-keepers' equipment factory or the dole.

I tried all three. And others.

Well, the Ford factory is now a shopping centre – sorry, "mall". And blokes who just a few years ago were putting cars together, and earning a decent wage for a man's day's work are now trussed up like some kind of kiddies' entertainer fetching fried chicken or burgers for blokes half their age. Or they're sitting in a call centre phoning people up at 7pm and asking them if they want double glazing or to change their gas supplier. Men doing women's work just to keep their dignity. Muppets.

The bee-keeping place is still going strong. I actually managed to last a week just after I left school. Let's just say the foreman and I didn't exactly see eye to eye. Result was he ended up on his arse amongst a load of hives that were being loaded on a forklift.

Fuck him, he was a Palace season ticket holder – can you believe it?

Most of us had jobs, either working on the market, doing a bit of labouring, I even had a spell doing the traffic news on the local radio station until they sussed I was 14 and chucked me out.

Like most lads of that age, my mates and I went through a stage of petty thieving, shoplifting – one of our mob even went cattle rustling. Did pretty well too as I remember.

We were also great followers of the steaming scene – we'd mob up outside a shop and just rush in and help ourselves. It was a great laugh. One of the great successes we had was at the Cancer Research shop – we went through there like a dose of salts, those two old biddies didn't stand a chance. Quality.

Point is, we were all used to having a few quid in our pocket, and with that we were able to buy decent clothes and afford to travel away with the team. Sure, you could bunk the train and occasionally jump a turnstile to get in the ground, but you did always need a wad in the pocket for incidentals. Booze, brasses, Charlie. Having a few quid was a pride thing. There's nothing lower than a geezer who turns up with a mob and spends the whole day poncing drinks and smokes off everyone. OK, if you're on your arse your mates will gladly finance a day or a night out but just don't make a habit of it.

So, with the usual ordinary routes of employment out of the question due to lack of qualifications or an inherent disability to kiss arse, most decent lads have followed a Thatcherite route and set up on their own, just as Colonel Sanders and that geezer McDonald did. Take a look at all the small businesses around you – most of them are run by faces. Having your own set-up means there's no-one to ask for time off for Boro away midweek. Try getting a plumber or sparks when England are in the European Championships or the World Cup. You'd better turn the stopcock off until we're knocked out.

While some of the kids there came away with bits of paper telling all and sundry what good boys they'd been, how they'd kissed the arse of the headmaster and were now ready to do the same for some poxy boss man, I left with something much more important. Friendship.

The kind of friendship only boys like me can understand.

I don't mean having friends to play golf with or go to a Round Table meeting with. I mean having friends who will stand beside you when you're outnumbered ten to one on a dark wet street in Leicester and being attacked by a mob with bricks and baseball bats.

I'm talking about the bond of trust between lads that will never be broken. Yeah, I can see your eyes glazing over. You don't understand, and I don't really expect you to. Unless you are a boy, that is.

You see, your idea of having a friend you can trust is probably being able to rely on them to water the houseplants when you're on holiday. Maybe feed the goldfish.

My friends would take a beating, or worse for one of their own.

Lads like me and my mates get nicked, have the shit kicked of us in the police van, have some more in the cell and not bat an eyelid. We won't give the OB the satisfaction of seeing us shaking with fear or crying like a baby. "You can make one phone-call, son."

"Yeah? Let me ring your missus and ask her if she wants some more of what I gave her last night." Crash, there goes another tooth.

We'll do bird, long bird and hard bird for our mates and not say a word. It's an unwritten rule. No complaints. Do the bird and do it without complaining. In the old days it was very different. If you were unlucky enough to get lifted on the day – then OK, you'd be looking at a fine – maximum. Even if you were nicked by the OB, more often than not they'd be pissed off by all the paperwork and either keep you in the cell until you'd missed the last train home, or – and the plod at West Ham were famous for this – make you do some mad things in the cells, just for their amusement. A kind of cabaret for the boys in blue. I never had the dubious pleasure of getting nicked at the Boleyn, but plenty of our boys did and they came back with stories of having to perform Noel Coward vignettes or build a model of the Titanic with matchsticks. Those West Ham OB were nasty bastards.

Still, if losing your dignity for half an hour meant getting away without being nicked and all the hassle of court – then fair enough.

These days, it's all CCTV everywhere. If you're a known face, the OB will be looking for you as soon as you get within a couple of miles of the ground. More times than I can remember, I've been having a quiet beer in a bar, sometimes not even on a football day when a plain-clothed OB will brush past and make himself known. "All right Aqua – behaving yourself?"

To be fair to them, most OB I've come into contact with have been OK. There are a few exceptions of course. The Merseyside plod have a reputation of being a bit mental. The top OB up there was the bass player with Freddie and The Dreamers, and if you get nicked at Anfield or Goodison you know you're in for a trying time. All the lads who have been pulled get put in a cell and this joker comes along and plays 20 minutes or so of his past hits. Not pleasant. Thing is, the police have a job to do – just as we, as top boys have a responsibility to act up. There is, I believe, quite a bit of mutual respect. The OB know who they are dealing with. They're not interested in the part-time hoolies – these lads who go and spend a grand or so on designer gear and hang about on the edge of everything, pretending to be a face. These are the muppets who go to pavement dancing classes. These classes were started by that ballet bird Darcey Bussell, who, when her busy dancing schedule allows it, will turn out with the Mansfield Town lads. As the story goes, she got caught up in a do with the Swansea Jacks, and noticed how all the lads started bobbing up and down during the off. She saw that their poise and balance was all wrong, meaning they were unable to give anyone a good shoeing as their weight was wrongly distributed. It's all on her website: <www.bouncewithdarceybussell.com>

Anyway, the whole thing took off and now there are dozens of these classes cropping up all over the country. Taking over from line-dancing, apparently.

You see the police see football as a fucking great day out. They're all on double-bubble, all the tea they can drink, and they're given carte blanche to get stuck in and give some lads a right doing. Nice work if you can get it. Most of them are just itching for it all to kick off. Let's face it, has to be better than nicking some poor fucker for parking on double yellow lines.

There's no doubt that the police and a good mob have a lot in common. Both will stick together and work as a team.

Lads like us will steam into a mob of OB to try to get a mate free, stand and go toe-to-toe with the Soul Crew, BBC, Zulus, ICF, Derby Silly Fuckers, Plymouth Sea Brethren, Carlisle Nasties.

Not all at once, obviously. We'd be annihilated.

It's the same kind of bond soldiers had in the trenches in the First and Second World Wars, exactly the same unspoken dignified kinship that unites true warriors the world over.

That's what keeps my friends and I forever together. Together forever.

After having a few games under brother Steve's wing – it was time for me to go to games with a few lads my own age. Bit of a youth set-up. Wasn't difficult to put together – I'd started to bump into a few lads my age who had either come to the game, like me with their brother or Dad, and it just seemed natural for us to start travelling to games together.

Away days at that age were one big adventure. Our lot were in awe of the older lads who were all ready to act up on a moment's notice.

Dudley Dudley who came from Dudley, Irish Steve, Hull Rod, Unorthodox Nick, Bad Tempered John, Panathinaikos Dave, and the biggest hooligan you're ever likely to meet, Gary, all took us under their wings and kept an eye on us.

We were like their mascots, getting them beer and fags, passing on messages between train carriages, reading their Tarot cards. They'd give us a few cans, let us have a few draws on a spliff then tell us great stories about their past offs.

The journey would fly by as we heard first hand about historical run-ins with all the major hooligan firms.

How they took the home ends at Stoke, Burnley and Hull. Then there was the Battle of Bury in '79, The Stockport Set-To of '82 and the Unpleasant Incident at Huddersfield in 1988. Go look 'em up. They are all there in the history books. No bullshit from our lot, I can tell you. Except for Unreliable Warren but he was soon made persona non grata for his outlandish exaggerations and make-believe offs.

We'd Lord it up in First Class, playing cards and getting plastered.

If we could get away without buying a train ticket, all the better.

More often that not, the ticket collector would know full well that we didn't have tickets, let alone First Class ones, but, let's face it, what was he going to do about it?

That's right: Jack shit!

On seeing a mob of a dozen or so lads plus us youth firm, he'd simply turn a blind eye and head off down the train to bother some scarfers, with our words of support ringing in his ears! Who knows, maybe these guards were boys themselves once. And a scarfer is just a scarfer after all. Go bother them, pal.

It was on one of these trips that I got my second taste of an off. It was a taste that will live with me forever. Little did I know all those years ago what a rich, diverse, fulfilled and thoroughly enjoyable life I would lead on the back of these very first skirmishes. I don't often go to church, rarely consider the meaning of Easter and hardly ever read the Bible before I nod off for the night. But I can tell you that every now and then, maybe with a tear in my eye when I'm thinking back to those good old days, I don't mind admitting I offer up a prayer to Him Upstairs in thanks for the day I came face to face with what would be the driving force in my existence for the best part of 30 years: football hooliganism.

# CHAPTER THREE

# All at sea with Vatican City

WE'D drawn a non-league team away in the first round of the FA Cup. Our opponents were to be Stonehenge. Our lot were, at the time, probably the most clued-up firm in terms of the opposition. Over the years the senior lads had long given up on the notion of being rewarded for their bravery in the traditional manner. Other top boys were sloppy. They'd return from battle expecting a few beers, a curry and a shag after a night in a club as a reward for their bravery. With us, it was different. Once we were back on home soil, a carefully selected debriefing team made up of lads who, for one reason or another, couldn't attend that day's match would meet us.

Returning warriors would be whisked away to glean as much information about the enemy as possible. That is how we came to have such a wide knowledge of the firms, crews, mobs and mugs, who we considered to be the opposition.

But we knew fuck all about Stonehenge and any potential offs to be had. A few reconnaissance missions later and we were in receipt of the necessary information to prepare for our trip.

We had learned that not only were Stonehenge getting the results on the pitch, they had built up a tidy reputation by giving it big style to both the firms of Wookey Hole and Westward Ho! in the preliminary rounds.

It was after the Wookey tie that the Stonehenge firm even made headline news in their local rag. After the game, which they'd won 2-0 with the help of a brace from a certain Steve Claridge (who went on to bigger and better things, of course), "The Casual

Druids" gave the Wookey crew a right chasing round the ancient stones until the OB arrived.

Our information was thoroughly researched. We learned the Hole boys had been hopelessly outnumbered, but they stood, and you had to give them respect for that.

A nice touch the Druids had mastered was instead of leaving a calling card as many of the firms did, they'd leave a crystal in one of the pockets of their victims. Non-league or not, that's got class written all over it.

The cup clash was looming and we knew we were in for a day of fun and games. Bring it on!

A week or so before the tie word got up to us that the Stonehenge lads were really up for it and they'd have a couple of white witches and even a wizard running with them.

Whatever, it was obvious these boys were no mugs.

Our mini-bus left at what seemed the crack of dawn, there were eight of us onboard, five top boys and three of us youth. As soon as we set off the older lads broke open the beers and smokes, by the time we'd made the motorway the songs were being sung and spirits were high.

We pulled into Stonehenge just before noon, got parked up and found the nearest boozer.

I couldn't help but notice a couple of the pub windows were boarded up. I asked one of the barmaids and she told me that was the result of the previous Saturday. Glastonbury had been the visitors, and there had been a lot of old Arthurian/Mystical scores settled. One of Glasto's top boys had come in with a serious firm all best dressed in full Lancelot gear. Fair play to them although I'm not too sure our lot would ever go that far.

The tart behind the jump went on to explain that the whole place went up, a number of the Druids getting some serious batterings from a firm of lads tooled up with Excalibur replicas. Those bastards can do real damage, believe me. Things were becoming more and more interesting. What were we in for? What were they in for, more like?

We knocked back a few pints, met up with a few other United lads who'd travelled down and made our way to the ground.

Outside the boozer there were a few Junior Druids, about my age. You could tell these bastards a mile off with their hoods and wooden staffs.

The main firm often used these younger lads as spotters, and sure enough as soon as we stepped out they disappeared, obviously off to let the Stonehenge main boys know our numbers.

We managed to pick up the obligatory OB escort who made it clear from the off they weren't taking any nonsense.

All in all there were around 50 of us, mostly serious United with a smattering of youth. A decent turnout whichever way you look at it.

We passed by the sacred stones and were about 200 yards from the ground when all of a sudden a hail of bottles, half-bricks and what have you rained down on us. The Casual Druids had got up on top of the stones and we were sitting ducks. They had the lot up there, camp fires, naked virgins, witches cauldrons, the full monty. It was impressive stuff.

As we were trying to protect ourselves from that little lot, a blood-curdling yell came up and around 100 more of the bastards came at us from the side. This lot were covered in woad and just had on skimpy loincloths. They were through the OB escort and on us before we knew what was happening. It was on top big style.

What happened next more or less put me on the map United wise.

Being badly outnumbered, the lads on the edge of our mob took a real beating, and this caused a lot of our boys to get on their toes and sprint back towards the pub. Running is so often looked down upon and too a degree I can see where critics of legging it are coming from. But sometimes self-preservation kicks in and this was one of those times. Or so I thought.

I have to admit, I was more than ready to join them, but before I could really think I was going toe-to-toe with a Druid.

"Stand lads, stand," shouted one of our main boys. For some

reason the call did the trick. No more backing off, we were going to give this our best shot and see these bastards off once and for all, and sure enough that's what we did.

The fact that we didn't all run for it seemed to take the wind out of their sails and all of a sudden the tide began to turn.

A few of the Druids had been relieved of their loincloths, but even naked they fought like demons.

There was blood, glass and woad everywhere. It was messy and for a good while it was difficult to fathom which way things were going to work out. Then we started to get the edge and that led to full-scale victory.

We were able to give a number of them good hidings until the OB arrived looking like something out of Star Wars, all tooled up and ready to baton anything that moved.

We felt we'd made our point, and not wanting to be nicked and then spending a few nights enjoying Druid OB hospitality, we thought it was prudent to duck out and get in the ground.

Once in the away end, there was no doubt I'd arrived as a United face.

I was immediately surrounded by a lot of lads, some who had been involved, others who just wanted to know what had gone off.

A few of the older boys were a bit sheepish as they'd done one and left the business to some youth.

It was pretty obvious who'd been at the sharp end by the woad, and I remember one of our boys waving a couple of loincloths around. Trophies.

Personally, although obviously loving all the attention, I was more than worried about getting back to the mini-bus in one piece.

But, all in all it was a great day. United went on to piss it 3-0, and with that the home lads seemed to have lost heart.

The trip back to the transport was a cakewalk.

We cruised out of Stonehenge and were back in the local boozer for last orders with yours truly getting plenty of attention from a lot of the main faces.

I've never drunk so much free Stella, nor eaten so many free packets of nuts. This was what it was all about. The camaraderie. The belonging. I was now one of them.

Being one of them of course, means my first love is my club. I'm United through and through. No messing. You want it you can have it, mate. We run from no one. Well, only sometimes. But I'm not too fussy where I get my fix. A row is a row ain't it?

Pretty soon after the Stonehenge scuffling, I met some lads who followed a national team, and I'm no different. There is one big difference, though.

Obviously, most boys go with England, and indeed I've been on many trips into Europe with them. I had season after season of fun on the Continent. Trouble is, you start to get noticed. The OB get to know who is running the show. For years it was yours truly. I quickly graduated from being a minor player in United's youth firm to a major player with England. My international career ran parallel with my outings for United.

Victories were many.

But things came on top and due to being involved in the major off in Charleroi during Euro 2000 I've had to keep my head down with England.

But I still get to go on European trips with my adopted country, the Vatican City.

Both my parents are devout Roman Catholics, so after I was told by the OB there was no way I'd be travelling with the England fans again, I took a look down the other fixtures in Europe.

One caught the eye, a Euro 2004 qualifying tie from Group 11, The Azores v Vatican City.

I got in touch with a couple of top Vatican boys through their website and I was made up that they were well keen for me to join them on their trip to the Atlantic islands.

The Azores had quite a rep mainly due to the mayhem they caused when they visited the Galapagos for the second leg of the World Island Championships a couple of years earlier.

They'd caught the Galapogos OB right off guard by sending their main mob up on a steam packet from The Cape of Good Hope.

None of the home spotters saw them until it was too late, and they ran the home firm around the Enchanted Islands, as they were called by Charles Darwin, for hours. The Azores boys were well up for it, game as, and many of the amazing species of wildlife, which are indigenous to the beautiful islands, took a slap.

Now I'm not going to give it the big one and try to tell you The Vatican City have a massive mob; that just isn't so. But what they do have is around 20 boys who know what it's all about.

Most of their support are scarfers and basically your average religious type, you know, nuns, cardinals, that sort of thing.

But like most teams they do have a few lads ready to act up if needed.

As it happened a few of the Vatican's top boys were travelling to London as part of the entourage who accompanied some Cardinal or other who was visiting David MacArthur, the Catholic Bishop of London.

A few emails later and I agreed to meet them at a boozer in London's Little Vatican area. Although a Londoner through and through, it was a part of the city I hadn't visited before, indeed, I didn't even know it existed.

There were a few VC restaurants and bars, and dozens, and I mean dozens of churches. Everywhere they were. These people really took their religion seriously, fair play to them.

I must admit, the old ticker was beating a few beats faster as I sat in The Fantastic Pope pub. I've met lads from all over in my time as a face, and in all those years I've never really had any problems, but I'm old enough and ugly enough to realise something could easily go pear-shaped.

I'd been in there for twenty minutes sipping at a Benedictine, when a young altar boy popped his round around the door. Clocked me then turned on his toes. He was obviously a spotter.

A few moments later the doors opened and in came a tasty looking little mob of six lads. They went to the bar, ordered a bottle of red wine and came and sat down at my table.

They all wore Cardinals' robes with all the accompanying

accessories. These lads were dressers, no doubt.

Their top boy was a lad named Joe. Holy Joe I called him. He was VC born and bred and had been on the scene for quite a while. By day he worked in the Pope's maintenance department, generally repainting crosses, servicing the PopeMobile, that kind of thing.

His mob were all a bit younger, and obviously a bit in awe of our man Holy Joe.

His first question was why would I, one of the top boys from the United firm want to run with the VC boys?

I could tell from his manner, that he was suspicious. Maybe he thought I was OB, perhaps he had a hunch I had been put up to it by The Azores lads.

But, as the wine and herbal liqueurs began to slip down, defences were lowered and we realised we had a lot in common.

And that's basically what I've found the world over, whatever colour your skin is, wherever you come from. If you love football and you're proud of your team, you're ready for a row.

I told Joe and his boys that due to our boys in blue I'd been barred from travelling with England, much to my disgust. I'd had some great days in Europe, but all of that was in the past.

In the old days a big England mob would turn up in some one-horse town in Spain, Italy or France and basically take liberties all day and all night.

But now the European OB had caught up with their English counterparts, and got involved with CCTV, spotters the lot. If you weren't nicked there and then, then once you got back home, the local plod would pay a visit.

The appeal of running with the VC boys was their mob could travel all over Europe, at least for the time being, without any OB being interested.

The first thing I did was ask the Vatican lads how we were to travel down to the Azores. For most of my previous trips I'd either flown or taken the train. There's nothing quite like turning up at Gatwick or Heathrow at 7am and seeing the bars full of faces getting stuck into the Stella at breakfast time. Train journeys are great too for a relaxed boozy day listening and telling stories of previous offs. But it was clear from the start that this little excursion was going to be a very different proposition. The VC boys were well sussed, and knew that the Azores OB would be on the ball and ready to keep a close eye on any top lads turning up. The game was to be played on the main island of Santa Maria and that's where the OB would be expecting our little crew to make for. Joe told me that we'd be heading for the smaller island of Pico, where we had a bit of business to attend to with some sardine fishermen who had taken a few liberties when the Vatican City had played the Azores in a friendly a few seasons earlier.

I mentioned to Joe that I wasn't aware that any of the islands other than Santa Maria had an airport, he told me that this was the case. This got me wondering how we were going to get down there, Joe just grinned and asked me if I'd heard of Thor Heyerdahl.

No, he wasn't the Danish lad Newcastle signed a few years back, and no he wasn't the top face at FC Copenhagen. Joe popped open a beer and told me he was about to give me a history lesson. This Heyerdahl character was a big name in the exploring world. He snuffed it back in 2002, but during his time he set about expeditions and stuff all over the shop. One of his outings was sailing, and get this, a raft made out of balsa wood across the Pacific. This was to prove that Peruvians could have sailed to Polynesia in ancient times. Why he wanted to do that, I have no idea. Personally, I'd rather watch paint dry than get involved with a load of old Peruvians but there you are, it takes all kinds.

Anyway, this old raft was called the Kon-Tiki, and after old Thor got pissed off with it he flogged to some guys who Joe knew. These characters lived in Venice, and would let the VC boys use it if they needed some ocean-going transport. The Kon-Tiki had been refurbished, and now boasted a couple of bars, carvery and casino, all mod cons to keep our firm well-refreshed during the voyage. The trip to the Azores was to take two days and nights, and including a match ticket the whole package came to £189, which is good value in anybody's language.

So, the great day arrived, and we all tipped up in Venice. Now there's a place. No streets, just canals...hundreds of them. Not a place I took to, I have to be honest. Full of ponces and nonces, sitting around in cafes and going to opera and that. Rubbish. All the buildings were hundreds of years old, all old fashioned and covered in dreary statues and pictures of Jesus and that.

As we gathered at the bar on the jetty waiting for this raft to turn up, I had a look around at the crew Joe had put together for this little jaunt. Including Joe and I, we numbered 12. A nice number, not too many to get the OB suspicious, but more than enough to deal with any unforeseen problems on the voyage. There were a couple of Cardinals, still wearing their purple robes with a Stone Island design I hadn't come across before. Quality. The youth section was made up of a trio of altar boys with angelic faces but Joe had already warned me not to judge these little books by their covers. When the moment came, these lads were the business, and I was to witness that sooner than I had expected.

There we were, minding our own business, having a couple of beers and a smoke, looking forward to getting on the Kon-Tiki and setting sail, when a couple of gondoliers strode in and ordered a beer. One of them sidled up to Joe and whispered something in his ear. I thought nothing of it, and just assumed the geezer was a face from the past. The gondoliers drank up and left the bar, and I thought no more about it. But it was obvious something was up, as the whole mood seemed to alter. The VC lads started jabbering away in foreign, but although I couldn't understand a word of what they were banging on about, it was clear that the gondoliers had come in to have a pop at us. Joe explained to me that there was a mob of twenty of these lads on the Bridge of Sighs, and they had sent their spotters over to let us know they were up for a row. Joe looked at his watch and told us there was plenty of time to have another couple of beers and deal with the gondoliers before our balsa wood raft turned up. The plan was for half of our mob to nip out the back door, cut across a couple of canals and through St Mark's square, hop on a vaporetto then lay low near the Accademia Bridge. One of the Cardinals led the boys out, whilst Joe, me and the others got stuck into a couple of grappas. After twenty minutes, Joe signalled that it was time for the rest of us to make our way to the Bridge of Sighs.

Just as we set off, we saw the Kon-Tiki docking at the jetty, so Joe nipped over to tell the skipper that we'd be back in half an hour and then he thrust a handful of euros into the old seadog's hand and told him to go and have a couple of beers on us.

It was interesting to see Joe at work first hand. It was obvious he was held in very high esteem by his boys, and it was an impressive little firm I was part of that marched past The Bell Tower of St Mark's towards our rendezvous with the gondoliers.

As we rounded the corner near the bridge, a shout went up, and it was obvious the home boys had spotted us. We picked up the pace a bit, and moved towards the bridge. Immediately a couple of plastic chairs were thrown down on us, followed by a hail of bottles and ashtrays. Joe shouted for us to keep going and get on the bridge. We were heavily outnumbered, and initially the gondoliers gave a good account of themselves, putting a couple of altar boys and a cardinal on their arses, but slowly we began to gain the upper hand and push the garishly dressed boat pilots back. For a couple of minutes it was even-Steven, with both firms exchanging slaps toe to toe. But one thing the gondoliers weren't expecting was the second half of our mob to pitch up behind them, which is exactly what happened. From there on it was all down hill, or all down the steps for the gondos. They seemed to suddenly lose their appetite for the knuckle, but the only way off the bridge for them was over the side and into the canal and that was the route they took. One by one they leapt into the water, away from the bother. The only problem for our boys was not pissing ourselves laughing as we watched the spectacle of twenty gondoliers swimming across the canal and scampering onto the opposite bank.

The tourists seemed to think it was some kind of ancient Venetian pageant, and I saw dozens of Japanese and American visitors recording the events on video cameras. I mentioned this to Joe and he shouted for all lads to make sure they we were all hooded and scarfed up just in case a video of our antics fell into the hands of the Venetian OB.

It was high fives and handshakes all round for our mob, and we made our way back to the jetty for to board the Kon-Tiki.

The raft really was the dog's bollocks. Incredible to think it was made of balsa wood. We went back to the bar to pick up our bags which the barman had kindly agreed to look after, had a quick beer with Benito, the skipper. He seemed a decent enough geezer, typical sailor type, even down to a patch over one eye.

He was keen to hear about the off with the gondoliers, and was pleased they were given a hiding. Apparently, there's always been needle between the canal boys and the balsa wood raft lads.

So, at last we jumped onboard and our trip in earnest began. I was bunked up in the same cabin as Roman Catholic Paulo, who was a decent lad and had done himself justice on the Bridge of Sighs. Once again we found ourselves of interest to the tourists, but it did stagger me that these people didn't have anything better to do than video-tape us setting off out of Venice harbour. I mean, what's the big deal about an exact replica of an ancient Peruvian raft made of balsa wood crewed by a mob of football hooligans from the Vatican City sailing out of Venice on their way to an off in The Azores? These people should get a life.

We immediately hit the bar and began to drink the raft dry. After an hour or so I was treated to a rendition of all the Vatican City fan songs, all performed in an operatic style by the lads. I've heard all the mobs sing, but I had to take my hat of to the VC boys, this was real singing. Benito the skipper was more than happy for some of the lads to take the wheel, and it was a real buzz to pilot the Kon-Tiki on the open Mediterranean Sea. At around 3am, I was bushed, and so decided to turn in. A few of the lads were deep into a card game, so I bade them goodnight and hit the sack. Paulo was already fast asleep, so I tiptoed into the cabin and stretched out. Lying there in the dark I wondered just how many lads like me had experienced such a day.

The sea was calm and the sun shining brightly as I gazed out of the little balsa wood porthole the next morning. I left Paulo asleep and I wandered into the galley for a bite to eat. One of the negative points of travelling with the VC was the state of their breakfasts, they were all mad for the continental style stuff. You know, strong coffee and a couple of measly croissants. I thought I'd turn them onto what me and my lads start the day with, so after getting permission from Benito I dipped into my bag and brought out sausages, bacon, black pudding, eggs, baked beans and mushrooms, the whole works. Within ten minutes the raft smelt like a greasy spoon, and the delicious aroma awoke the whole mob. At first they were a little suspicious of what was on offer, but after a couple of mouthfuls, the full English got the thumbs up and the lads demolished the huge pile of food.

After breakfast, out came the cards again and a good day's drinking began. After a few beers I popped up to the bridge to keep Benito company. The Kon-Tiki was making good progress, we were approaching the Straits of Gibraltar, and then it would be out into the Atlantic. The Med really was like a millpond, and Benito left me at the wheel whilst he went for a beer and a couple of hands of cards.

The day passed quickly, and the balsa raft stood up easily to the waves and currents of the mighty Atlantic. There was another night on the beer, and this time I was the one to do the entertaining. I gave them the full repertoire of club and England songs, and I took the opportunity to debut a couple of my new compositions that I had planned to give an airing at the next United game. "Spurs, You're Going Nowhere, Quick" and "The Day United Gave Leeds A Good Hiding" were both well received by the VC lads. I was pleased to listen to some good advice from of the top singers who told me that perhaps the chorus to the Spurs song should be in B flat and not G, advice I took, and I tell you what, he was spot on.

Another good night's sleep was followed by breakfast, but alas not one of my specials as all my provisions had been consumed, so we feasted, if that's the word, on ships biscuits, rum and limes.

Benito reckoned the limes were to ward off scurvy, which was fine by me.

By mid-morning the Azores was visible from the Kon-Tiki's crows nest, and the atmosphere on the raft changed somewhat.

I've found that no matter which firm you deal with, the characters are mostly the same.

Before a big off, different lads have their own personal ways of preparing themselves.

Some of the boys wanted to be alone, a few stood quietly on deck, some carried on drinking and singing, a few took to Buddhist chanting. In my book, each lad has to find his own way of getting ready.

Soon, we began to come across the occasional Azorian fishing vessel, some of the boys wanted to raise the Vatican flag to let them know we'd arrived, but Joe wouldn't hear of it. He reminded everyone that the whole reason we were on the raft was to arrive on the quiet, well away from any OB. So, the lads just blanked the fishermen and we continued our progress to the Pico harbour.

Pico was a shit hole. Nothing more. Nothing less. A one horse town with a couple of bars and that's it. The air, the people, the streets, everything stank of sardines. Benito expertly piloted the Kon-Tiki to a quiet corner of the harbour, well out of the gaze of prying eyes. The plan was to sample the delights of the Pico night life, then see if we could find these fishermen and give it to them big style.

The two bars were El Sardino and Sardino-Sardino. Sounds great, eh?

We decided to split into two groups to sample the delights of both establishments. Joe, the lads and I shuffled into El Sardino and ordered the beers. It was obvious we were looked on as interlopers, strangers in a locals' bar. The talk at the bar was fish, fishing and more fishing. After an hour or so, one of the locals came over to our table and asked us if we liked sardines. We replied that they were OK. This obviously wasn't the answer he was looking for, and he started to get a bit lippy, basically saying that any man who didn't love sardines was a homosexual. His mates at the bar backed him up, and all of a sudden things began to get a little tense, all over a sodding fish. The fishermen obviously had no idea who they were dealing with, and thinking we were just a bunch of tourists started to take liberties. The lad with all the chat then went too far when he dropped a fish head into Joe's pint.

It all happened very quickly. One minute the crew of fishermen were standing around us giving it the big one, the next they were either on their backs or on their toes.

Again, I was well impressed with the VC lads. They were quick, very handy and didn't muck about. They were handing out slaps right, left and centre and the fishermen just didn't know what had hit them, literally. The row moved out onto the harbour, but the trouble was more and more fishermen started to appear from their cottages, all tooled up and ready for a ruck. Fortunately, the rest of our mob could see what was happening from the other bar and they were soon right in the thick of it. But, despite doing our best, things began to get a little out of hand. No sooner had we decked a couple of fishermen, another half a dozen appeared from nowhere, all bright-eyed and bushy-tailed.

I could see that even Joe had taken a couple of hits, and I was feeling the pace after a handful of maggots had been shoved in my face. But the cavalry was about to arrive in the form of Benito. Our skipper had seen what was on the cards and had slowly but surely guided the raft across the harbour to where it was all kicking off. Benito shouted for us to jump on board, and with the pressure rising all the time, we were all more than ready to take his advice. Joe shouted to retreat to the Kon-Tiki, and one by one we leapt onto the raft and safety, although a few of our foe wanted to continue the action onboard our boat. This was a big mistake, as the half dozen or so who did make it onto the raft took a terrible hammering as our boys stripped them naked then threw them in the drink.

So, our low-key arrival on the Azores had not been as low key as we had hoped. As we headed back out to open sea a police helicopter swooped down over us, and a few minutes later two police launches arrived manned by OB armed to the teeth. They instruct-ed Benito to weigh anchor and let them board. Our skipper was well aware that it was pointless to attempt to outrun the police boats, so reluctantly we pulled to and allowed them on deck.

The Azores OB didn't really know what to think of us. Joe tried to persuade them that we were simply tourists who had lost our way, but one of their number was a police spotter who immediately recognised most of our firm. He radioed ahead to Santa Maria nick for them to get some cells ready. A couple of the OB threw a line from one of the launches and instructed Benito to tie it to the mast of our raft. So, we suffered the indignity of being towed into the port of Santa Maria under police arrest.

OB are the same the world over, and these clowns on the Azores were no different.

There was a huge police presence at the harbour, and as soon as we landed we were bundled into the back of a meat wagon, and driven at speed to the nick.

Back at the big house we were strip-searched, finger-printed and our mug shots snapped before being locked up for the night in a dirty, flea-ridden cell.

An hour or so later a big bowl of some kind of fish stew slop was dumped into the middle of the cell but it was so revolting, none of our lads were interested.

We all spent a sleepless, fitful night chatting about just how we found ourselves in our sorry state.

The next morning we were shepherded into the police yard where we were stripped naked and hosed down by a couple of guf-fawing OB. After that gentle start to the day, we were locked up again before the Vatican City's man in the Azores turned up to give us grief. I decided to keep a low profile and stand at the back of our firm, not wanting to be spotted as an Englishman. The suit gave us all the usual stuff these planks normally do. You know the script, you're a disgrace to your nation, the scum of the earth. Blah, blah, blah.

Yeah right.

The upshot was that the Kon-Tiki was to be immediately towed out into international waters by the OB launch, and we were then to set sail back to where we came from straight away. We were warned that if we thought we could simply wait for the police launch to disappear from view then navigate our way back to Santa Maria we'd be staring at a three-year stay at a lovely cell not unlike the one we were presently in.

The Azores OB wanted us off and away from their islands ASAP, so we were told to get in the meat wagon immediately. Back to the harbour we sped, and there was our raft, surrounded by a couple of dozen OB. A couple of TV crews and a gaggle of Azores top boys who were hoping, just to rub the salt in, that they could get a pop at us. But it wasn't to be. The law kept the Azores lads at arm's length and rushed us on the Kon-Tiki. There was Benito, at the wheel. He too had spent a night in the clink, and was not the happiest raft skipper in the world.

With cries of derision from the home lads, our vessel was towed out of Santa Maria, and away from any further aggro. After an hour or so, the launch stopped and the OB released the line, leaving us to our voyage home. So, another two nights on the Kon-Tiki was ahead of us, with no booze and only half a box of sea biscuits to last the journey.

Oh, and Vatican City were gubbed 4-0.

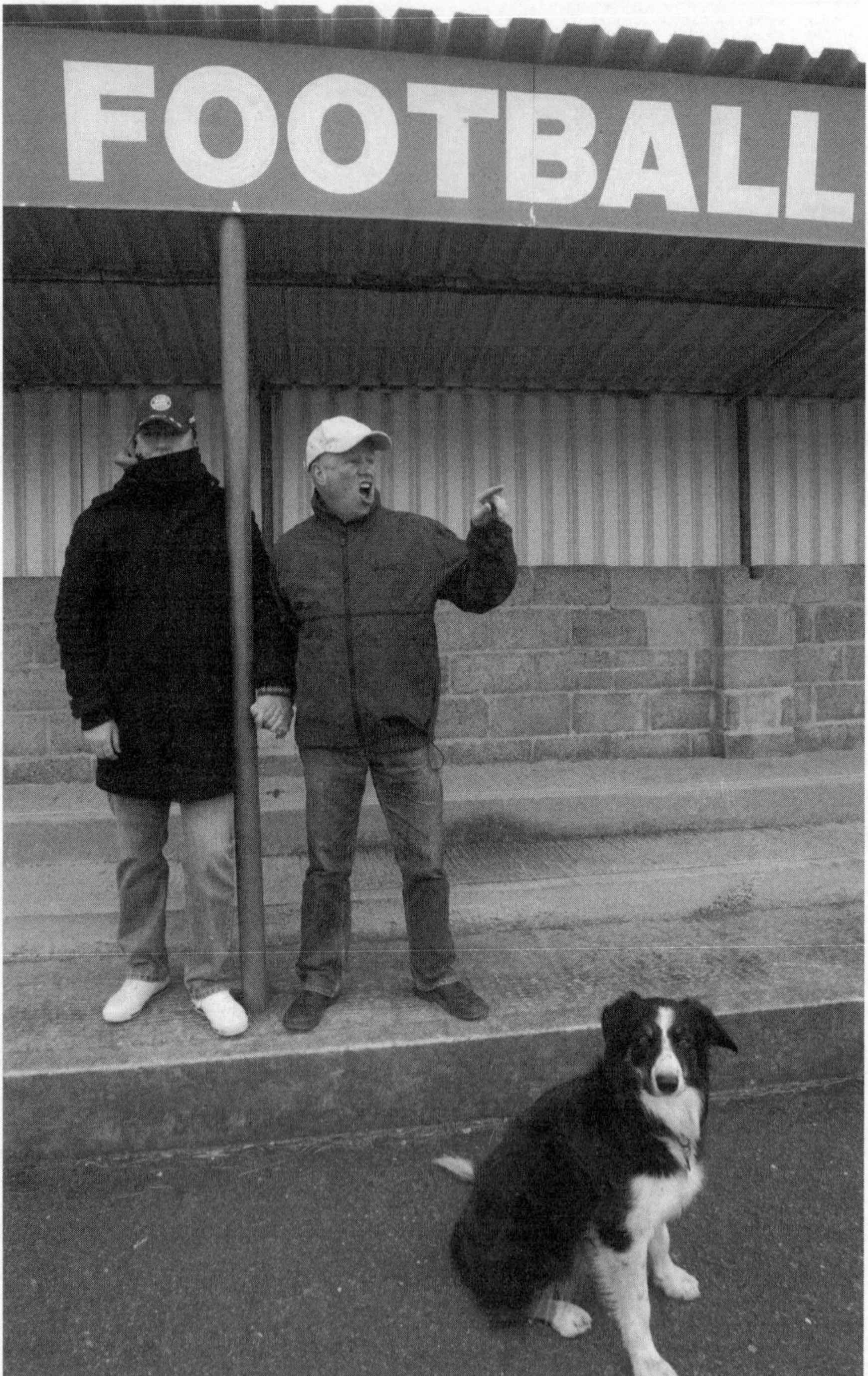
FOOTBALL

# CHAPTER FOUR

# Mobs, movies, scribes and scraps

LIKE you I've read books written by so-called social experts who have all been to Oxford or Cambridge. Well, I've been to both and never seen any of them.

I remember steaming into the London Road end at Oxford in the mid-80s and there wasn't anyone with a mortarboard on, just a couple of hundred geezers from the Blackbird Leys estate ready to tell you your fortune.

I've also read a stack of books written by so-called top boys and their firms. Most of them could have been written by Hans Christian Andersen, some people's imagination!

These hoolie books are flying out at the moment, all supposed to tell it like it is. There have been quite a number of references to our firm, and they're the ones that really make me laugh.

For instance, in *Steam Into The Plums*, by Gary Lee, the author reckons after a League Cup tie his Portsmouth firm ran us all around the docks, onto a ferry which then left for France, where we hid amongst the lifeboats.

According to Gary and his tome when the ferry docked at Le Havre his mob chased us off, through a farmers' market and into the station, where to escape a beating we jumped on an express train to Nice, arriving on the French Riviera some six hours later.

Gary, my old mate, you've got to be having a laugh, haven't you? Are you stretching the truth to make a few extra quid at our expense? Is the flower stall outside London's Waterloo train station not bringing in the dough it was once? I'm not going to tear his fanciful tale to pieces. Just to say that if you took the bother to check your timetables, Gary, you'd discover that an express train from Le Harve to Nice doesn't exist. Truth is we had to change in Paris and then had a 35-minute wait before boarding our train. Fair enough, we were on our toes but stick to the facts, eh. Gary? Enough said, you plank!

Of course, Gary isn't alone when it comes to telling porkies about our lot. Some people seem to have made a lot of money on the back of fibbing about us. Word of warning, boys. We always get payback.

In *Stand You Mugs*, by brother and sister casuals Colin and Anne Parker-Bowles, they reckon they came to our place with their QPR boys, took liberties then went shopping at Liberty's in Regent Street. Fact is Liberty's was closed that particular day for a refurb. I know because I was supposed to be taking back a faulty toaster for my sister. Admittedly, the Rangers lads were out in force and I haven't got a problem with Colin and Anne boasting about their numbers. Well impressed. Fair play. But their boys shot off to Harvey Nicks to shop after the game. Liberty's...I ask you!

And so it goes on.

Basically anyone who has been a bit of a face on the scene and can operate a word processor is able to put over his or her side of the story. Fair enough. As with these examples, the reader has to take it all with a huge pinch of salt.

Likewise the internet. There's been a proliferation of hooligan sites with plums and nonces just queuing up to post absolute bollocks. After any main off there'll be boys who "were there" telling their side of the story.

Of how they ran the rival firm, clashed with the OB and were back in the internet cafes half an hour later to tell the world about it through the information superhighway.

I'll admit swapping email addresses with some of the nation's top boys in order to make plans for meeting up. I'm not massively up to speed with it all but sometimes needs must. As with mobile phones, you have to move with the times when it comes to organising times and places to get it on. But it can have its pitfalls. I admit to once sharing correspondence with someone, who I thought was the top boy over in Dundalk but, having miss-typed the address, had a bizarre email conversation with a 62-year-old widow who was looking for love and thought I was too. I was. Not with a 62-year-old bird, though. That's just sick. Unless you are a 62-year-old bloke, that is. But then, you'd fancy younger birds surely?

Sites such as www.inter-row.com and www.ruck-finder.co.uk can be quite helpful when you are in a hurry but the best way has got to be a quick phone call on the actual day of the match. That way you hopefully get more of a feel for what you're being told.

A fairly recent innovation on the net has been Firms ReUnited and a bloody good idea this is, too. An old mate of mine, Nosher Norris, came up with the notion one lazy afternoon while on a holiday in Thailand. Nosher, whose days running with the firm were long behind him and who had made some serious money by starting an online auction house flogging snide togs, www.fakefashion.com, was nursing a cold beer in the Dog's Bollocks bar in the beach resort of Pattaya when the light bulb switched on. The bar is a well-known meeting point for top boys taking in the sun, sea and sex over in Thailand and Nosher was encouraged by the reaction of other lads sinking a few beers before heading off to the brothels. Two months later, aided by a grant from the Prince's Trust Nosher was up and running. To date, Firms ReUnited has more than 30,000 members and is said to have re-united double that. The Dog's Bollocks can be a dangerous bar to go poking your nose if you are not a face and claim you are. The owners are retired hoolies from Arsenal and Chelsea whose identities I will have to withhold for my own safety. Go in, mention the book, enjoy a cold beer and admire the sexy Thai girls in Chelsea shirts behind the bar. Some of them have even got Chelsea tattoos. Mind your own business; take in the football hooligan memorabilia adorning the walls. But they'll soon suss you if you bowl up and start giving it the big one. These boys know practically all there is to know about the game and probably know the top boys in your firm. Mostly, though, they are all about keeping the peace and only occasionally come out to play, usually with the Jocks who run a Celtic bar in the resort. They never have got on but the Thai police do a reasonable job of keeping a lid on it and for the most part it's a good time and not a good row that is the order of the day. Oh, and do yourselves a favour, keep the Thai girls sweet with the offer of a cold one now and again, eh?

For me, Firms ReUnited proved useful when I staged a firm reunion and I had little trouble tracking down all but one of the lads who was on the infamous Ibiza Town away trip back in 1985. One missing from 25 ain't bad. But then they don't have the internet in heaven do they? RIP Rob Wilde.

Authors were the first to bring the exploits of hoolies to the great British public but the British film industry didn't wait too long before jumping on the bandwagon. Hooliganism has got the lot, after all. Heroes, villains, fight scenes, booze, drugs, sex and long walks. Although the sex bit never really appealed to me during the heat of the battle. Not so a real top boy by the name of Squiffy Cliffy who used to run with an elite bunch of bleeders who attached themselves to Notts County's Trent Insidious Turnouts. Squiffy was always on the pop, hence the name, and also wouldn't go anywhere without a bird on his arm. Sometimes it was his missus Thelma, sometimes it wasn't, if you know what I mean. Top hoolie maxim: What goes on tour, stays on tour. Unless you don't like the bloke, that is. Anyway, no sooner had these TITs steamed into some plums or other looking for a jolly along the riverbank in Nottingham, than the Squiffster would sneak away for a bit of the other. Dirty so and so. Not that he is likely to feature in any Hollywood blockbuster on the trials and tribulations of soccer yobs terrorising their way around our little island any time soon. It has always amazed me that the Yank movie moguls haven't brought us a Tinseltown tribute to what is, without doubt, one of our national sports...fighting at football. I reckon they'd cast planks such as Brad Pitt as a Chelsea Headhunter or what about Joey from Friends as a Man City Guv'nor? Uncle Sam? Bollocks to them. The Yanks have never come up with a big-budget film but there has been a shed load of British films that have come out over the years trying to tell the tale of civil unrest at football. But how many films have got it right, told it how it really is? Got to the bottom of the whole deal? None, that's how many. A big fat zero. Nish. Nothing. Nowt. These lazy bastards make a film with a couple of hard-looking actors and claim it's a life-like portrayal of football hooliganism. Bollocks. You can sit through any of the offerings and count the mistakes one after the other. It's laughable stuff. Trouble is, though, I ain't laughing. It's an insult to me and my kin, you, yes you reading this book: my brothers.

Top boys wearing cardigans with sandals for God's sake. Geezers smoking pipes and supping real ale, discussing their next mission of mayhem in the snug of some shithole. I mean, I ask you. But that's the sort of tripe you'll get if you ever have the misfortune of watching a little know Film Four production from the early Nineties entitled *Crews, Casuals and Chaos*. It gets worse with this offering. The central character is a mug called Barnaby March, a public school educated nonce, who would never cut it in the real world as a leading player. The only such top boy I've ever come across was a bloke called Guildford Tim who was a face at Southampton. He was actually expelled from Charterhouse for taking a firm over to Guildford Grammar School for Boys and legging the entire school; pupils, teachers and even the janitor. Fair play, Tim. No, you need to avoid this one, it's a complete waste of time.

The plums at Film Four are not alone though, dear reader. Oh no. There are others. And loads of them. For ever and a day they have been getting the terrace fashion all wrong when it comes to recording it on celluloid. I've lost count of the times I've choked on my Mint Imperials or spluttered out some popcorn while watching this pathetic crop of films, which are a complete embarrassment to the industry. Bet they still think their movies have credibility because some knob at the Guardian reviewed it as a "bold, brutal and shocking piece of work which is both a frightening social statement and a brilliant cinematic debut from Etienne Markoff".

Bollocks! In *Fortune's Always Hiding*, a film that is loosely based on the notorious antics of West Ham's Inter City Firm running around England like a load of lunatics, we see geezers bowling around in Lycra leggings with retro Winfield trainers. It doesn't get much worse than that. OK, there was a short period in the early Eighties where leg-warmers made an appearance over Lois cords to compliment a spanking pair of Adidas Trim-Trab. But Lycra leggings? Never, mate, never. No self-respecting thug would have been seen dead in Winfield trainers but there is a reason for these being used, which I unearthed during a bit of nosing around over at Upton Park. Story goes that Frank Bryder, the man who put the finances together for poncey-named Markoff to make this pile of crap was also an entrepreneurial cove who bought job lots from bankrupt companies looking to shift serious amounts of stock for a bit of cash. Turns out he had untold pairs of these plastic monstrosities and insisted the *Fortune's Always Hiding* costumes department took them off his hands, despite protestations from the film's hooligan expert advising on the shoot, a very young Ben Elton. Ben Elton banging on about football violence? I know. I pissed myself at that one, too. I can just imagine him at the front of a mob fronting up some hellbent nutters from Middlesbrough, can't you? "Just because we don't share the same allegiances when it comes to the support of a particular football club, it doesn't mean you have the right nor need to thump me. If you do, mind my glasses". More of Mr Elton later.

Winfield's finest ferrying around one of London's if not Britain's biggest hardcore firm? Big mistake, Frank. These days Frank has scaled down his empire considerably and is a market trader in Bethnal Green flogging dodgy DVDs and cheap flannelette nighties shipped in illegally from Uzbekistan. I've spoken to him about the fashion faux par and he admits it was a clanger. But Frank has paid his price and I know for a fact that he took a good few slaps from top West Ham lads who weren't best pleased they were portrayed in such an unattractive way. Frank isn't alone when it comes to these cock-ups, though.

In *Hardnut* starring John Inman as a camp yob with a serious mean streak we see loads of fellas piling off a train at Liverpool Lime Street looking for the off. Nothing wrong with that you might think. No, not if some of them weren't wearing pashminas, that is! In the same film untold Millwall Bushwackers come marching along outside the Tate Modern in London in headscarves (although, to be fair to that lot it was terribly windy during their scene). So rest easy Frank, there are some proper plums still ballsing things up when it comes to getting terrace fashion to look authentic. Another area of concern for those with an eye for detail is the fight scenes. There's only one word to describe these: totally wrong. When they do get it on with other firms in the films, it's laughable stuff. Somehow they can't crack it, can't get the buzz, the fear, the adrenaline-fuelled highs, over on screen. If they wanted it how it really is, these film producers, they should get someone like me on board. Yeah, I could do that but they'd have to pay me big bucks. I mean, I'd have to give up the day job, wouldn't I. Day job? Yeah, right! Would I get my own trailer on the film set? Too right I would. And it'd have my name on the door with a couple of golden stars thrown in. I can just see me and some of the boys lording it up and giving these luvvies a bit of what for.

Casting seems to be another area for concern. Directors, producers and the film-making industry in general don't have a clue as to the make-up of a top boy. And I'm not talking about a bit of lippy and some blusher either. They can't call on their university education to decide who can portray the right characteristics. They can't get inside our heads, dear reader. Can't quite crack it. What makes us tick. And do you know why? 'Cos unless you've been there, actually been in the frontline at somewhere like Elland Road trying to put on a decent show against Leeds; unless you've had your head stoved in by a tasty firm of Cardiff at Paddington after nipping to the loo and losing your mates; unless you've hidden in a furniture shop as a load of Aberdeen Casuals try to finish the job they started on you some ten minutes earlier, then you will never know what makes us like we are. We're not animals. Well, only sometimes. And that's what these film-types don't get. They can't pigeon-hole us 'cos we're not pigeons. Never will be.

Take 'Aving It With The Divs, starring Ray Winstone, for instance. Fair play, to Ray, top boy and all that and, I understand, a big, big West Ham fan. But when Ray and his little crew bowl up to the rival mob's boozer to batter them they get it all hopelessly wrong. Most firms would send a top boy in to offer them out for a scrap in the street and then pile round the corner from a hidden vantage point to outnumber their foe and record another bloody victory. But what does our Ray, snarling Cockney accent and all, do in what is supposed to be the movie's climactic ending? He starts gently throwing pebbles at the windows to attract their attention! It just doesn't cut the mustard. Ever thought of ringing the bloody doorbell, Ray? You were good in Sexy Beast, though. Better than Ghandi, anyway: "Your name's Rowntree, the Grosvenor, you'll be there. Yes, yes, yes, yes, yes." Love it.

Then there is the disastrous casting in Riot FC: A Yob Odyssey. What plummy-voiced, public school educated knobhead fresh out of university cast Julian Clary up against Rowan Atkinson as two main mob leaders terrorising Sheffield in vicious turf wars between United and bitter rivals Wednesday? It made the film a laughing stock and here's the rub: It wasn't supposed to be a fucking comedy. Again, I've heard the Wednesday lads felt Atkinson played his part quite well and mastered the Sheffield accent nicely but United's Blades Business Crew were livid that Clary was cast as one of them. What's even more galling for these city of steel psychos is that Clary beat off competition for the lead role from none other than top Blade and top man Sean Bean. I know Sean through a third party and he was extremely pissed off not to land the role. Sean is a devoted Unitedite and even has a tattoo, which reads "100 per cent Blades" on his arm. Or something like that. The only blade Clary has is a pair of those poncey roller blades for cavorting with others of his persuasion in places like Brighton. So I'm told.

Of course, nothing could compete with the sheer magnitude of the number of fuck-ups in Mug Me Off At Your Peril, set in

Jockoland, Scotland to you and me, which was a total balls up from start to finish. First off they had St Mirren's infamous Love Street Division as main rivals to Montrose's Portland Bill Seaside Squad. I know for a fact that these two firms get on quite well and even arrange quiz nights on the first Wednesday of every month with any monies raised donated to local kids charities. Fair play, lads. And Celtic Casuals' top fella had a weekend job as a barman in an Orange Order Social Club in Milingavie, on the outskirts of Glasgow, for fuck's sake! You'd never see that, not in a million years. And when Rangers ICF's hard-as-nails leader Wazim Patel (played by Akrim Patel) uses his turban to stash a Stanley knife it just doesn't wash. Fact: The first place plod look for hidden weapons on a Sikh hoolie is in his fucking turban.

Dear, oh bloody dear.

That's fiction, of course. When it comes to so-called undercover documentaries, there have been some howlers, too.

Ever heard of the documentary maker Zion Hughes? Course you have. This jumped-up piece of shit stitched up a top crew of hoolies for an undercover film he made for a series called *Hughes In The Mix.* What he did was simple but unfortunately for the lads involved, very effective. The story goes that Hughes had heard the whisper that there was a mean little crew causing havoc down at Conference side Crawley Town and they were happy to shout the odds at the drop of a cold can of Stella. Only they didn't bargain for this plank turning up on the manor and ruining their fun and games big time. In my book, not literally as in this one but by way of a figure of speech, these people are worse that any OB I've ever come across. Even those who will dish out a beating with truncheons while questioning your parentage...at least they let you go after administering a good battering.

Hughes went undercover to see what exactly was going on and for three months he sat in the firm's main boozer, the Blue Lion in Crawley High Street, chatting with locals and making out he was a baggage handler at nearby Gatwick Airport. He even brought regulars "luckies", items, which, he claimed were found on planes after being left by passengers. Clever. In fact, he was getting them from the local Matalan store just up the road. In time this knobhead managed to get in with a couple of faces by buying them a few beers and acting the flash so-and-so and giving them lifts to away games in his new Clio. Hughes' story was that he was over from Northern Ireland where he had knocked about with the strongly Loyalist mob who followed Linfield. A lot of Crawley lads have links with Glasgow Rangers and share their politics and he was soon in as one of them, running up and down the country, fighting all-comers and generally getting up to no good. In one sickening piece of footage, a lad called Sticky Bob 'fessed up to stabbing a St John Ambulance man up at Wigan and then openly laughed with derision as Hughes, torn for a minute, asked him if felt no guilt. That little slip of the tongue earned Hughes an admonishment. Sticky Bob's moment of bravado cost him the little matter of ten years in nick.

Hughes was filming the bloody lot and managed to get a two-hour documentary out of it which, he boasted on his personal website, "lifted the lid off the terrifying world of soccer yobs".

Those who write books and produce movies rely heavily on the press for their facts. They shouldn't. This lot are worse than hoolies. And I should know I used to have a paper round.

There's no such thing as bad press, is something I've often heard. That's bollocks for starters. What about the Watford Observer or the Bucks Free Press? But the bad press I'm on about isn't the plank on the Daily Mail turning some silly buggers' scuffles at Selhurst Park into the "worst soccer hooliganism we've seen for years". Oh, no. The media can't wait to have a dig as soon as it kicks off anywhere near a football ground but for years they've been firming up to start trouble then retreating to the press box to write it up.

For yonks they have orchestrated rows, backed off and were first with the exclusives.

This is the gutter press, one that you will never have seen portrayed in their true light. Until now. We have 'em on their toes most times but they have had their days. One of the Paperboys' finest hours came at an England Under-21 friendly in Split back in 1984 when they chased the Yugoslavian press pack out of the ground and back to the city centre, fighting and writing all the way. There were portable type-writers, dictaphones and notepads scattered everywhere as the English press pack pelted their foreign colleagues with anything to hand. I saw it all. It wasn't pleasant viewing. I enjoyed it, nonetheless. But that's me.

It was the same old story when they were collared by the Slav OB back at the Irish boozer The Dublin Up, drinking to their success a little later on. "What us, we were just doing our job, in the name of bringing the truth to our readers," they bleated as one. Clever boys. Of course, they can get away with it because they are the ones who report back to Blighty. And guess what? Another rake of banning orders are duly dished out to those suspected of causing the rucks. That is how their unpopularity started and now, whenever anyone can get to them and have a pop, they will. Domestically, the power wielded by the press firms doesn't tally to that with actual mobs. Millwall's scribes, mostly from the South London Press and Evening Standard get legged everywhere frequently, for instance. Birmingham's answer to Zulu Warriors is a two-bob crew from the Brum Evening Post. Their so-called top boy, 'Nutty' Nigel Shingle, writes the gardening column under the name Greenfingers and pretends he's a football colour sketch writer on match days just so he can run with the firm. Leeds' Yorkshire Post Army have never matched Elland Road's finest and Cardiff's best efforts come from a 21-stone, balding sub-editor from the Western Mail. We have had run-ins with the Paperboys and I've been there to witness some of their top offs. After a particularly nasty encounter over in Ireland, where we had a run-in with the Provisional IRA before a friendly against Shamrock Rovers and had to back down rapidly when they brought out half a dozen ArmaLite rifles, we were propping up a bar in the city centre waiting for Fastidiously Tidy Tony to meet us after he went back to the hotel to change his togs. The scribes there to cover the match were in and there was a bit of banter in the air. The Irish lads outnumbered the Brits and our lot smiled as the tone turned nastier and nastier. It was like a boxing match...and I do love my boxing. In one corner sat Fleet Street's finest, filling the air with quips about huge expenses claims, while not ten yards away, the Spudeaters suffered the verbal sparring and threw a few heavyweight insults of their own. I sensed a change in the seriousness of the matter when The Daily Telegraph's pompous chief soccer writer Howard Thomas, clearly pie-eyed from too many Guinesses, started ripping the piss out of the grammatical errors and sloppy structure in Seamus Flynn's observations in that night's Sports Green Final. "Do you even know what a split-infinitive is?" he asked, mockingly as Flynn turned puce. "Your intro is too long and this third paragraph changes tense in the middle," he continued. "Do yourselves a favour and get a transfer to features, my old son," implored Thomas, in between more swigs of the Black Stuff. My knowledge of how the press works is limited but even yours truly knows there is no greater slur than that. Features? It's a graveyard, I am told.

Flynn was on his toes and wading in within seconds and the whole place erupted. Me and the boys stayed cool and let them get on with it. After all, it wasn't our beef. The Paddys got whacked and by the time the Mick cops got there, we were on our plane home. Incidentally, on another trip to Ireland with our firm's literary group, for a visit to Oscar Wilde's house at One Merrion Square, in Dublin, we had it with a horrible bunch of boys who go by the name of Waterford Crystal Palace, a tidy crew of Irish fans of the London club. But that's another story.

# CHAPTER FIVE

# Phone-ins, moan-ins, Mellor and mayhem

THROUGHOUT the 70s and 80s cashing in on the slaps, beatings and calling cards dished out by Britain's hardest mobs would have been unthinkable. Various Governments, ably helped by the arse-licking Press, came down heavily on the pursuit of a punch-up at football. We got sick of the times some ponce of a politician would use the "sickening problem of football hooliganism" line to try to win votes. There would be regular dawn raids and nickings and guess what? Yep, the TV cameras and reporters would just happen to be passing at 5.30am to record the brave boys in blue swoop on a few lads who had probably done no more than Lee Bowyer and Keiron Dyer in that infamous scrap at St James' Park in the name of Newcastle United. The OB got their orders and were happy to oblige. A quick tip to the media, and, well the rest is on the six o'clock news that night. I can just imagine the sad, moustachioed cozzer tuning in after his steak and chips and can of Tesco two per cent lager, cuddled up to some chubby bint who loves chocholate more than she loves him. "Ooh, look Denise, that's me knocking down that nasty football yob's door first thing this morning, luv. Aren't I a brave little policeman," he'd tell his lardy Doris. Get a life, mate, eh? And Denise, leave the Maltesers alone.

And yet, more often than not, the real top boys would have the last laugh. Very few of them ever got nicked and if they did suffered no more than a few years in chokey, a banning order or a slap on the wrist in the shape of a £200 fine. Chicken feed to a main face. Obviously, the time behind bars would have hurt a little. You'd be missing games after all. And what do games generate? As much fucking bovver as we can cause.

General elections would be the worst time. There would be a calm before the storm. It was coming. We all knew it. The OB knew it. The dim-witted general public didn't. Top boys often used to call a halt to any activity as a general election approached. Instead of seeking out rival crews, the lads would honour a truce and meet up in various boozers to try to fathom out which particular mob would be targeted by the party trying to stay in power this time around. Back in the Margaret Thatcher regime, the Tories had a real thing about trying to nail Huddersfield's top fellas on account of former Labour Prime Minister Harold Wilson being a native son of the Yorkshire town. That's just sick, Maggie.

That's not to say these power-hungry politicians didn't face rebellion in their attempts to snaffle our finest hoods for a stint of bread and water and lights out at eight. One top boy, a lad from Coventry City's Sky Blue Hatchet Division we called Ballot Box Donald, even tried to stand as an MP one time. He was, he said, representing the FFFF (Freedom for Football Fighters) but the poor sod couldn't read and write properly and he ballsed up the paperwork. His bid came to nothing, although the name still stands to this day. Go to Highfield Road and you'll see the four Fs scrawled and daubed on the surrounding walls and lampposts. Anyway, sure enough the raids would come a week or so before whichever Prime Minister was in power went to Her Majesty at Buck House to ask our purple-rinsed head of state to dissolve parliament. Northampton's Get Stuck-in Crew would suffer an early morning knock one time, Real Madrid Ultras (London Branch) the next. It was sickening. Manipulative politicians taking liberties. Fat cigars on the back of some decent boys doing a bit of bird. The OB loved it, of course, and the talking head with a couple of pips on his shoulder who came on Newsnight after the court appearances to give a gloating account of how his force "smashed this evil, unremitting and hardcore gang" made us puke. So the idea of someone actually harnessing the power of hooliganism into a business venture would hardly have been a vote-winner or deemed acceptable in those dark days. Today, as we know, things are different. The mood all started to change when that plank, and, yes, former politician David Mellor got his own radio show. His derisory '606' show went out on Radio Five Live and was one of the first talk shows for fans. Pleb after pleb would ring in on their way back from some shithole up north and complain about "the lone striker, David, it's just not working". Mellor would give it some, trying to pretened he knew what the fuck this twat was on about despite being happier prattling on about some woofter in tights on a ballet stage. It was two hours of torture for us thugs and very often we would opt for some music – anything from Barbara Streisand to Stiff Little Fingers in my case – in the car instead. But then we got angry. Very angry. A couple of us had taken far too much and, heading to London for a night out after a match at Watford one Saturday in December decided to do something about it. Big Tim was the driver and as he pulled his Merc up outside Broadcasting House, the Mellor droll went on. "Next up is Glenn. Now you're on the way back from Colchester and are rather unhappy with the linesman, Glenn, is that right? Why has he irked you so, I wonder?" drawled the buck-toothed, bulbous-jowled joker, not realising that, nice a guy as Glenn is, he has never once in his 30 miserable years been asked what irks him so.

"Keep it on, mate," I said. "Give it five minutes and let's see if we can liven the conversation up a little bit for Mr Mellor's army of listeners."

Tim stayed in the driver's seat and me, Frank and Lillian (Frank's missus) got out of the motor and headed towards the entrance. Bold as brass, we strode past the white pole and into the security gatehouse. "Hi, we're the Waterlooville String Quartet and I'm afraid we're running a little late for a guest slot on Tonight with Fred Dineage," I gave it in my best upper-crust voice. Earlier I'd clocked a story in a copy of SAGA magazine that Tim had in his car and seen that the former Magpie presenter Fred had just got a show on BBC Radio 3, Music and Musings. (Good lad, Fred, although he used to wear a syrup. Pompey fan actually, no, wait a minute, he's actually a director at Fratton Park. Can't get a bigger Pompey fan that that. Well apart from that nutcase John 'Portsmouth FC' Westwood with the body full of tattoos and that bleedin' drum.) "OK, get your breath back, this is the Beeb, not Checkpoint Charlie," said a rather genial, capped security guard. "Now, you should all have passes but no doubt you've forgotten them seeing as you were in a rush. No problem, squire, I can easily issue you some new ones." It was then that our new mate spotted my error. "Quartet? You're missing one. There are only three of you." Lillian spoke first. Thank God she did. I was about to bundle the old codger into a cupboard and rifle our passes. "That's why we're late. We had a car crash and our driver was killed. We thought about cancelling but, well, it's what Cyril would have wanted," Lillian said gently, through mock tears. "You don't get too many opportunities to play for Fred, do you?" she sobbed.

He seemed moved. "Quite right, miss. Sorry to hear about your friend. OK, here are your new passes. Up you go. Studio 5, it's next to the 606 studio."

Bingo.

Within a matter of minutes we were in Mellor's studio. It was kid's stuff. Barged past some bird wearing a headscarf and glasses holding a clipboard, opened a door and that was it. Lillian had a little bit of knowledge on the decks from her time at college and some work experience on her local radio station Spirit FM and took control after we'd locked the original operator in a broom cupboard.

"Now, what's going on here?" stuttered Mellor as he clocked us over the rims of his bins. "I have to tell you, regular listeners of 606 that the studio appears to have been stormed and I know not what they want from me. Would you kindly leave? I am trying to conduct a radio phone-in here. This isn't very welcome I must say."

I grabbed a spare microphone and gave him what for. "Mellor, we've had to put up with this shit for too long. It's boring bilge and with no due respect, you are hardly the man to talk football with the nation's fans. You used to support Fulham before you swapped to Chelsea for fuck's sake. We want the remainder of this show to be a proper fan phone-in. A hoolie love-in. Where's our voice? This is discrimination. So all you top boys out there, all you who have been chased this afternoon, got a good kicking or had it with the OB, phone in and tell Mr Mellor the true state of our game now." We had seized the show, stolen the airwaves. Job done.

For the next hour and a bit the phone lines were red-hot and to be fair to old Mellor he did a fine job. With our help he weeded out the plums and got the main fellas to air quickly. Some had heard my rant and came to air giving it large but kept a nice spirit about their tone. Others unburdened themselves with genuine grievances about the state of their firms and their rivals. They made their points and Mellor led the discussion quite skilfully before moving on at just the right time. In between, security guards tried to force entry to the studio but Mellor and his colleagues had warmed to us in some respects and were on our side to a degree. (Later, some sections of the Press suggested that Mellor was suffering from Stockholm Syndrome, which describes the behaviour of kidnap victims who, over time, become sympathetic to their captors. Also see Patti Hearst and the Symbionese Liberation Army). They had never experienced anything like the number of calls before and they seemed to go with the flow. With the help of the bird with the clipboard and the deck controller who we had let out, we kept the guards and then the OB at bay. Lillian made tea and Mellor even offered round some Custard Creams from his satchel. They had been converted. "This is real radio, let the people speak," the bird with the glasses kept saying. And so it went on until the clock inched towards 8pm.

"On that note, John from Carlisle, we'll have to leave it. I'm David Mellor and this has been quite the most extraordinary 606 in my time here. Next up, the news with Len Ganley."

We opened the door and gave ourselves up. Mellor promised to put in a good word for us and we were carted off to the nick, while he made his way to the Garrick. The press we got was unbelievable, but, inevitably, I suppose old Mellorphant couldn't resist going back on his pledge to tell it how it was. He portrayed himself as some kind of hero, held at force against his will, despite what can only be described as a polished and professional job of leading the country's first hoolie radio phone-in. The Sunday red-tops ran with headlines such as "Mellor: My soccer yob hell" and "Hero Mellor's thug ordeal". Radio, TV and the internet buzzed with our coup. By mid-week, broadsheets such as the Times and Telegraph ran essays from eminent broadcasters such as Jimmy Saville and Max Hastings both applauding our takeover. "Where would we be now if Oliver Cromwell hadn't sensed the weakness in the Roundhead army and made himself captain of the cavalry? Haven't these people, hooligans or otherwise, done the same thing?" asked Hastings. Saville's piece ended with "I, for one, applaud them".

As for Mellor, well, true to form, he came out of the whole thing smelling of the proverbial roses. Or did he? His time with us re-ignited his political career and for a while he was everywhere. The work flooded in and you couldn't pick up a paper, turn on the radio or receive a message from a carrier pigeon without seeing, hearing or reading Mellor's views on everything from the Spice Girls to chewing gum goo-ing up our streets. Eventually he stood as an independent after the death of Cyril Fletcher, MP for Oswestry South and was duly elected. But within a year he had resigned over his alleged affair with actress Antonia de Sanchez. The Sun told us he had romped with her after insisting she wore a Chelsea kit. Antonia later confided to me over drinks at The Flying Scotsman, Kings Cross, that it was a Fulham away top. His resignation led to events coming full circle for Mellor. One media mogul decided to take a gamble on a radio phone-in he had heard Mellor conduct a couple of years previous.

Former national newspaper editor Kevin McKendle was the chairman of The Transistor Group, owners of the hugely popular and successful TalkSTARS station. McKendle was a tough-talking, no-messin' type and had often employed tactics and the language from the working class area of London in which he had grown up. He was a keen Millwall fan. He had long nurtured the idea of a talk radio station for those who preferred their football a little rough around the edges. And so it was that McKendle launched TalkSLAP, Britain's first radio station with the hooligan in mind. The format was simple. Get four sets of two show hosts to cover morning, noon and night. One of the duo would have to be a retired top boy, the other whose background was in broadcasting. Then, let them at each other with the help of endless phone calls from plebs with nothing better to do. Intersperse with endless, repetitive ads and jaunty, over-the-top jingles and sit back and count the revenue. McKendle brought in loads of former top faces and paired them up with the professionals in two weeks of trials at his London HQ. He eventually settled on the following weekday presenter and schedule (with thanks to TalkSLAP's website):

"6am until 11am
*Morning off*
*Gary 'The Gas' Ellis and Keith Chegwin bring early-bird hoolies their unique double act. Ellis is a former face at Everton and Chegwin, an ardent Koppite. Ex-copper, DC Nigel Ward, who was Tranmere's spotter for a decade, calls in for a regular daily chat to give the OB their say. It's sparky stuff!*

11am until 4pm
*Bob and Zed: Uncut!*
*Zed Tyler, one-time head honcho of the feared Tampa Bay Rowdies firm, brings an American slant to proceedings. Seeing things rather differently is Robert Kilroy-Silk. It's knockabout stuff. Charlie McAlpine provides all the latest prices on the scraps at today's fixtures. (See Charlie's website, <www.oddsandsods.com> and catch him and his guests on his evening satellite show on AtTheOffs.)*

4pm until 8pm
*Evening kick-off*
Presenters Larry O'Leary and Eamon Holmes are at the helm. Larry, a Didcot Town fan, has served 12 years for football-related violence. He's a reformed character and a respected author on

hoolies. Manchester United fan Eamon has been prised from TV. The issues of the day are discussed.

8pm until 8.30pm
*Intermission*
The lads enjoy a break. Music from The Corrs, The Doors and Fun Boy Three (changes nightly)!

*8.30pm until midnight*
*Fight Night*
Manchester City's retired Guv'nor Teddy Longbottom hooks up with Michael Fish to take calls on hardcore hooliganism, with a special slant on the good old days.

Midnight until 6am
*Through the night*
Former Talksport presenter, Chelsea fan and writer for comic Harry Hill, Paul Hawksbee, chats to all those night owls out there about their hilarious moments during rows. Comic interludes from Tottenham-supporting sidekick and former fashion boutique manager Andy Jacobs."

Yep, TalkSLAP was a huge success and, of course there was only one candidate to host the flagship Saturday night phone-in. Spot on, our old mate David Mellor. It was simple. And it worked. Witness this transcript of one of the more colourful shows...

"Hi, and welcome to 7.07 – the football hooligan's phone-in. My name is David Mellor and for the next two hours I want your calls on what's happened in the Premiership, the Coca-Cola Championship, Leagues 1 and 2 and of course the non-leagues. Where was the knuckle handed out? Who was on the receiving end of some serious slaps? Who took liberties and who were on their toes? And who saw your top boys and were immediately well up for it? So let's get those phone lines humming, it's 7.07! And to kick the show off we've got Terry who's a Burnley fan and he's on the M6 on the way back from Turf Moor.

*"Terry, thanks for calling 7.07, what's on your mind?"*

"Hello Terry, I mean Mr Mellor. First time caller, I'm a bit nervous."

*"Ha! No you're Terry, and please, call me David."*

"OK David, yeah we're on the way back from..."

*"Terry, would you be good enough to turn your radio down?"*

"Oh, right. Is that OK?"

*"That's fine Terry, now fire away."*

"Right, yeah we're on the way back from Turf Moor where we've had a nice little row with the Wolves lot."

*"Now as I believe, haven't Burnley got a lot of new faces in their firm this season?"*

"That's right David, and that's basically the reason for my call. Wolves came up here last year and gave us a right running, they spent the day basically taking liberties."

*"Terry, I remember that – I'd say that was one of your poorest performances for some time."*

"You're spot on David – last season was a big disappointment. But this year, we're unrecognisable from that mob. I admit, we're not the most exciting bunch of lads you'll see, but we're quick, well organised and we don't give you time to settle."

*"Now Terry, isn't that Big Ray who's now in charge of the Burnley lads?"*

"Big Ray, yeah that's right, he came in during the summer from Accrington Stanley, and he's really got us going up here. Fair play to him."

*"What's he done to change things up there?"*

"Well, he's brought a lot of young faces into the mob, released a lot of the older boys – most of them have drifted into the non-league scene, he's changed the tactics and given us a lot more confidence. He realises some of the boys need an arm around them, some need a kick up the backside now and again. It's not rocket science, it's basic man-management, David."

*"Yes, I'm looking at the stats now Terry and I must say they do make interesting reading. For instance in the Championship this season, only Leeds have handed out more slaps than you boys, but it's away from home where you've really impressed. That pub you burned down at Leicester a few weeks ago was superb and of course the way you forced the Lord Mayor's Show to be re-routed when you came down to West Ham was another great display."*

"I really believe David, if we can keep this firm together, we're going to get better and better."

*"I suppose Terry, the one fly in the ointment could be if one of the bigger clubs come and take a look at Big Ray. For instance, with all the speculation concerning Nasty Tony's future at Old Trafford, are you worried that perhaps Big Ray would make a move?"*

"It is a worry David, but when you see how much Big Ray enjoys what he's doing up here, I'm certain he's happy here. He signed a contract, written in his own blood by the way, and he's not going anywhere."

*"OK, well thanks for the call Terry and all the best for the rest of the season. Now, talking of what's happening at Manchester United – we have Martin on the line from Altrincham. Martin, welcome to 7.07."*

"Hi David. Great show as always."

*"Good evening Martin, now I believe you're not too pleased with the way things are going with your boys."*

"Well, that's a bit of an understatement. Nasty Tony's lost the plot David, he's not nasty these days, actually he's not even unpleasant – he's got to go. He's turning our firm into a laughing stock."

*"Yes, certainly, from the outside your mob does seem to be struggling at the moment."*

"David, today was a typical example of what's happening up here at Old Trafford"

*"Yeesss, Martin, I'm just looking at the stats here and it seems that you struggled today against what, on paper seem to be a rather ordinary firm, Bolton's Little Trotters. Indeed, before today the Little Trotters had really only put up one decent show on the road, and that was back in*

*November when they managed to spike the ball boys' half-time orange juice with some kind of hallucinogenic drug at Fulham. But today, by all accounts they gave you a bit of a surprise."*

"David, a couple of years ago we'd have dealt with these Little Trotters with one arm tied behind our backs, they would have got off the train at Piccadilly, we'd have been waiting, hit them hard – job done. But Nasty Tony has changed our tactics, no-one really knows what's happening, and now firms are coming up here and fancying their chances."

*"Yeeesss, Martin, looking here at the reports it seems the LTs caught you off guard."*

"Off guard? That's a bit of an understatement, David. I hope I've got enough time to tell you what happened, I know you have a lot of callers waiting."

*"No problem Martin, I'm sure all the listeners are interested in what's going on up at Old Trafford at the moment."*

"OK David, thanks. Right, well, we all meet up on Wednesday night at The Pitch Invasion as usual for a few beers and a chat about what we're planning for Saturday. All the boys are there, and we're all thinking this could be the opportunity for us to get back on track. You know, give the LTs a good slapping, get the confidence going again, then push on. So there we are, having a few Stellas, enjoying the excellent carvery, which by the way David is just £4.95 a head – how Darren and Kay do it for that kind of money, God only knows – anyway, I digress. So we realise Nasty Tony is conspicuous by his absence. Eventually, in he comes, but he's not alone, and get this, he's dressed in a turquoise tracksuit. With him, dressed identically is David Icke. So, well, you can imagine David, us lads are all staggered. No one knows what to say. So Nasty Tony and Icke sit down, order Perrier water and then Tony tells us there's a change of plan for the Bolton game. So, us boys, we're all looking at each other, you know, then Icke stands up and starts banging on about spiritualism and how, late at night, he sometimes turns into a lizard."

*"Yeeesss, Martin. I've heard about Mr Icke claiming he turns into a*

*lizard, I was at a dinner with Kenneth Clarke last week and someone mentioned this lizard business."*

"David, that's just the start. So you can imagine, us lads don't know what to say. Then Icke says there's no point in getting a crew ready for a row with the Little Trotters, it'll be a waste of time. So now, we don't know what's going on. Then Nasty Tony says he and Icke have some astonishing news about the Bolton game. Get this David, Icke says, 'Yeah – there's no point in getting a crew together for Bolton coming over because the world is going to end on Friday'."

*"Friday, Martin? Well, that was yesterday."*

"David, exactly. So Nasty Tony says, 'Well lads, there we are – you lot might as well have a few beers and prepare yourselves for Armageddon, David and I are going to have another Perrier water then go back to my flat and then we're going to a Pilates class at The Salford Spiritualist Institute.' So he and Icke get up, and just before they go to the bar Tony gives us all a crystal and says he'll see us on 'the Other Side' on Saturday morning."

*"Well, Martin, As you probably know I've been presenting this show now for more than three years, and I have to say that is really one of the most incredible stories I've heard. How a once mighty firm like yours has sunk to such a level really is beyond me. I remember just a few years ago when Ken Bates was chairman at The Bridge a number of your boys kidnapped him and shaved his beard off, and I believe it was only last season when your lot gave those Cossacks that Roman Abramovich had invited over to see the game a good seeing to."*

"David, I was involved in both those offs – in fact I've planted one of those Cossack hats up with herbs and alpines and put it in my garden, it really is a picture at this time of year."

*"So Martin, what's the future for your firm?"*

"Well David, you can imagine. After Wednesday night, we just didn't know what to do. Nasty Tony had told us the world was going to end – some of the youth, who dote on him, believed this was the case, some were in tears. These young kids are tough boys David, but they're only 15 or 16, and you know, if someone they trust and believe in tells them everything's up in 48 hours – well, they're going to take it badly. After Tony and Icke had left, we had a few beers and tried to sort a couple of things out. Basically, and I'm not trying to blow my own trumpet here David, I took control of the situation and attempted to put things on an even keel. But it wasn't easy. Some of the boys just weren't interested – their attitude was, 'Well, if the world's going to end, just what is the fucking point' – excuse my French there David."

*"Yeeesss, well you can perhaps understand their viewpoint."*

"Any road David, I had to sit there and basically see our firm fall apart. Fortunately, the dozen or so top boys could see all this stuff was a load of bollocks, and the lads who make the difference all said they'd be well up for it on Saturday. But the problem was numbers. You can have ten or a dozen really clued-up boys, but as you know David, if you're met with 80 or 100 Little Trotters as we were today, there's very little hope of getting a result. Basically, David, we were down to the bare bones, and fair play to the Little Trotters they made the most of it."

*"But Martin, what's the future for you and your firm? What's the situation with Nasty Tony, is he still running your crew?"*

"David, I ask you, how can he? He no-showed today, and as you know, next to noncing, poncing, grassing, being OB, not standing, not understanding simple orders, giving it the big one, giving it large, not protecting your own manor, slapping scarfers, not wearing a scarf when it's fuckin' cold and being City – that's the worst thing you can do."

*"I understand and completely agree with you Martin, so are you saying you're looking for a new boss up there?"*

"David, yes we are. I've been asked by a few of the lads if I'd be interested in taking over but I feel I've still got three or four years in me at the top level of hell-bent hooliganism. I really don't believe at the very top, you can combine the management tasks – you know David, taking in non-league and reserve games in mid-week to see if there are any young upcoming faces ready to make the step up and being ready to steam into a load of raggedy-arsed sheep-shaggers on a Saturday afternoon. So, now, here live on national radio I'm saying no, I'm not interested in the job at this time in my career."

*"OK, Martin I hear what you're saying – so who would you like to come up to Old Trafford and take charge of your boys?"*

"Well, David, it's not a job for an inexperienced lad. I'm well aware that there are a number of good young top boys on the scene at the moment. Lads who have come up from the various youth mobs. I'm talking about faces like Untidy Steve over at Bury and Punctual Howard down at Walsall. Sure, these boys have done the business over the last season or two, but with all due respect to them, they're just not ready for the fishbowl existence that is being top boy at OT.

No David, and I'm going out on a bit of a limb here and maybe I'll ruffle a few feathers, but I have two names on my list who I'd like to see come to OT and restore our firm to former glories. How about either former Chief Superintendent Maurice Callaghan, once of the Greater Manchester Police? Or how about Kippax Ken?"

*"Whoa there Martin, OK, I can see the rationale behind appointing Callaghan, but Kippax Ken – the main Manchester City top boy?"*

"I know David. I did say my suggestions were coming from the left field, but let's face it we're well into the 21$^{st}$ century now. To progress, we have to put aside tribal differences and look at the bigger picture. David, it hurts me to say this on national radio, but earlier this season when we went over to Eastlands expecting an easy ride, KK and his lads gave us a hard day's fight. What he's done there over the past few years has been incredible. I for one believe he would come to OT if asked."

*"Well Martin, thanks for the call – you've made some very interesting points there but really, I think you're having a giraffe if you think Kippax Ken would move across Manchester from City to United. Yes, there have been a few examples in the past, Denis Law and the fanzine writer Confused Dave – but for a mighty firm like yours to be led by an ex-City man, that appointment would rock modern British football hooliganism, which of course is what this show is all about. So let's get those*

*phone lines humming and on line four we have Bromley Steve who was at the New Den this afternoon and actively took part in a lovely piece of public disorder when Stoke were the visitors, but Steve has a problem with Stone Island's allocation for their new range of zip-up jackets..."*

Radio wasn't the only medium to latch on to the commercial value of hooliganism. TV executives at Channel 5 went out on a limb to screen the first ever British Football Hooligan Awards, dubbed the Hoolies. It was a move they would regret, ultimately. I took notes on the night and put together an account of exactly what went on during this ground-breaking occasion...here's what I wrote:

*Channel 5 schedule:*
*Wednesday 17th June.*
*9.00 pm. The Hoolies. Inaugural British Football Hooligan Awards live from Slaps in Leicester Square.*
*Presented by Jonathan Ross and sponsored by Bernstein lager, this country's top boys celebrate another incident-packed season.*
*Music from The Hollies.*

"Good Evening and welcome to The Hoolies. My name is Jonathan Ross and let me say right away, that never before has there been so much testosterone gathered in one room.

Blimey, evening the lap-dancing girls have five o'clock shadows. But on to the first award which is Best Newcomers, and joining me up on stage to read out the shortlist, please put your hands together for Mr Graham Norton..."

"Thank you Jonathan. Love that shirt, by the way. The four nominees for Best Newcomers are:

The Bad Men from Brentford.

QPR's Quite Physical Retribution. Love the name, boys.

The Ram Raiders of Derby County.

The Top Yourselves of FC Samaritans.

And the winners are: The Top Yourselves".

Steve Jones' voice-over: "What a fantastic story this is, The Top Yourselves were only formed in 2003 by fellow Samaritan tele-phone counsellors Lee McPherson and Barry Miller. Attaching themselves to FC Samaritans these lads have quickly built up a fear-some reputation, the pinnacle this season being their clash with The Kiddies in the Children In Need v FC Samaritans English Charity Cup semi-final at Villa Park."

*Lee and Barry take the stage, shaking hands with both Jonathan Ross and Graham Norton. Lee takes the microphone, brandishing his Hoolie (a gold fist on a marble plaque).*

*"What can I say? To stand here in front of some of the greatest top boys this land has ever seen with an award like this is really a dream come true. Barry and I were aware that charity football was badly lacking a decent firm, and I believe that this award confirms that our boys have now filled that gap. I'd just like to thank Suicide Stewart, Depressed Frank and Manic Depressed Frank. We couldn't have done it without you lads!"*

*Lee, Barry and Graham Norton leave the stage as The Hollies burst into* He Ain't Heavy He's My Brother.

*Jonathan Ross continues. "Well done lads, and take no notice of Graham when he asks to borrow your Hoolie!*

*"Our next Hoolie is The Lifetime's Achievement Award, and gentle-men, if you would be kind enough to take a look at the video screen over there, you'll hear from a previous winner of this prestigious trophy. The screen lights up, and sitting in a dressing room is infamous Millwall thug Dan "The Butcher" Harris.*

*"Hello lads, sorry I can't be with you tonight but I'm appearing as King Lear at the Tivoli Theatre in Dundee. I know most of you there, and I'm sure I've chased most of you round Bermondsey at one time or another."* (*Harris' speech interrupted by shouting from West Ham's ICF table*). *Harris continues: "Now, now lads, don't forget your man-*

ners. *The geezer we're honouring tonight has been on the scene since the early 1980s.*

*In 1985 he broke the all-time record for having it, when he brawled at 38 league games – a record that remains unbeaten today. (The TV camera zooms in on Barmy Ben Hamilton, leader of Sheffield Wednesday's Awful Owls). In 1988 he went over to Germany with the England team, and came back with the title of Europe's Naughtiest Lad awarded by the French hoolizene "Voulez Vous Un Slappe?" (Mechant Garcon Euro 88) – and may I remind you all that is this country's only international trophy since 1966. He has gone on to win this title four more times and in 1997 reached the pinnacle of our industry when he and his firm swept the board at the World Ultra Awards in Buenos Aires. Whilst many of his peers having moved on to other fields, myself included, this character has stuck with it and only last year hit the headlines again by winning I'm A Hooligan – Get Me Out Of Here.*

*Steve Jones' voice-over:*
*"Lads, top boys, nonces, ponces, grasses and spotters – put your hands together for Barmy Ben Hamilton!"*

*Barmy Ben walks up to the stage, stopping occasionally to shake hands with diners at other tables. He embraces Jonathan Ross, and to tumultuous applause holds the Hoolie award high above his head.*

*In a voice, choked with emotion Barmy Ben begins his speech.*

*"Lads, what can I say? It's been a long journey since those early days in the 1970s when my career began. I was a naive kid of 15 when I was involved in my first off. As we all did, I made a load of mistakes, but I was eager to learn. I watched the likes of Yorkshire Mick, Slippy and Jimmy the Hat go about their business, and I listened. And now, to stand up here with this Hoolie..."*

Barmy Ben has to stop, he dabs at his eyes with a handkerchief. "You see, it was a dream, a crazy, mad dream, that a kid from Sheffield could one day..." Again Hamilton has to stop, now he is in floods of tears, and clearly incapable of continuing. Jonathan Ross takes the microphone, "Come on lads, let's hear it for Barmy Ben Hamilton."

The room stands as one man, and applauds as Hamilton returns to his table with his award. The opening chords of *The Air That I Breath* crackle through the PA speakers as The Hollies strike up again.

Ross, clearly affected too by the emotion of the moment has to blow his nose and wipe his eyes before continuing. "If I may just have a few seconds to gather myself. Phew, that was really something.

"Well gentlemen, we now come to the climax of the evening, Firm of The Year, and with the nominations, give it up for Mr Brian Sewell.

Art critic and broadcaster Sewell shakes hands with Ross and takes the microphone.

"I have seen the Mona Lisa. I have gazed in awe at the ceiling of the Sistine Chapel. I have been amazed at the complexity of a Mozart Aria and I have sat, wearing just a loin-cloth and daubed with woad, at dawn on Ayers Rock with a tribe of Aborigines – or Native Australasians as we must now call those little fellas – and witnessed a total eclipse of the sun. But nothing dear friends, has ever given me more satisfaction, or pumped more adrenaline through my veins than being part of the Ointment Crew who ran Darlo ragged in '79. Come on, if you want some, I've got it!"

By now, the diners – well refreshed after three hours of gratis Stella Artois – are more than ready to enter into the spirit of things, various shouts and chants are heard and a lit flare is thrown onto the stage from the Watford Force-Field table. Four Slaps stewards, dressed in yellow fluorescent bibs quickly rush onto the stage and throw a table cloth over the flare, two others manhandle Ross and Sewell back to the backstage area.

There is some kind of commotion at the Luton Town Milliner Squad table – "Same old Watford, Always Ruining Awards Ceremonies" they sing. One of the Watford party throws a chair which crashes into Yeovil's Wurzel Business Squad following who were enjoying the Tiramisu, distracted from their delicious Italian dessert, the now angry West Country men, on seeing Hull's Untamed Tiger Youth Mob laughing at their predicament presume the young Humbersiders were responsible for the missile. As one, Yeovil's finest launch themselves at their perceived attackers.

Within moments, the Slaps dining area resembles a Wild West saloon, no table escapes, or wishes to the violent mayhem.

The Hollies, ever aware that they, let alone their guitars, amplifiers and drums are unlikely to leave Slaps unscathed, bravely attempt a version of John Lennon's *Give Peace A Chance*. They are barely into the first chorus before lead singer Allan Clarke is felled by an empty Jack Daniels bottle.

Jonathan Ross returns to the stage in a half-hearted attempt to quell the rioting, but realising the situation has gone far past the point of no return, goes to the edge of the stage and aims a winkle-pickered kick at an angry member of Crewe's Railway Children.

The fire doors of Slaps burst open and in come twenty or more fully kitted out police riot-squad, wielding batons and spraying canisters of CS gas.

The arrival of the constabulary changes the mood of the drunken fighters, now instead of battling amongst themselves they quickly join forces against the common enemy, the OB.

The police, sensing they are wildly outnumbered form a protective shield around The Hollies, Jonathan Ross, Graham Norton and Brian Sewell whilst one of them urgently signals to Steve Jones and his production crew to quickly vacate their broadcasting position.

Steve Jones voice-over: "I have been instructed to leave here immediately, this tele-cast will now end."

Jones, his assistant Tasmin, sound engineer Nathan and 16-year-old Cheryl, on work experience, are led from their mobile studio by two burly police officers. More Met Riot squad have now arrived on the scene but too late to prevent the Ipswich Tractor Mechanics from setting the Slaps stage alight.

No-one ever discovered who had been voted Firm Of The Year.

The Daily Mail: SOCCER THUGS' NIGHT OF SHAME.

(Excerpt). The question that must be asked is whose bright idea was it to pack a West End nightclub – a football hooligan theme bar named Slaps –with the biggest thugs this country has to offer and feed them enough alcohol to fell an elephant?

What we saw last night was the result of too many years of Labour government.

The Guardian: SEWELL GAFF RUINS SOCCER CEREMONY.

Art Critic Brian Sewell poured shame on himself and his fellow critics last night at The Hoolies Awards in London. During his presentation speech Sewell claimed he had "writhed in pleasure whilst reading a haiku by Peruvian poet Jose Lopez-Guizana."

As all of you know, Jose was a sculptor – it was his brother Miguel who was a poet and produced the superb Lima haikus.

Website <www.topboys.com>

Site crashed due to over 80,000 hits as broadcast of The Hoolies ended.

# CHAPTER SIX

# Under Fives and girls with knives

EVER heard of a band called Half Man Half Biscuit? If you haven't you're a plum. If you have you're on my sort of wavelength. I've been to see the Biscuits a few times and always had a lot of time for them. They're Tranmere Rovers supporters, by the way. Anyway, one of their top songs contains the line: "Stromgodset Under Fives, did the offy by us." Now, I'm not making any statement of fact here but this could well be the first time any mention of what have become known as "youth" firms was put down as a lyric. Respect, Biscuits. But the point here is that when this tribute to Scandinavia's first ever youth firm came about all those years ago, no-one, not me, plod nor any of those silly fuckers from Leicester university at the, wait for it, Sir Norman Chester Centre for Football Research – who reckon they know the score when they know Jack Shit – could have ever realised how quickly the proliferation of these crews was going to be. As I write, I am aware of more than 50 such naughty little firms bouncing up and down the country, earning their spurs and eventually graduating to the main mobs. And they don't just fight other little 'uns, dear reader. Oh no. These emerging hoolies are desperate to fast-track their way to the real business of grown-up fighting and will do just about anything to gain the respect of the top boys, get noticed and get the nod to get on with the proper stuff.

West Ham probably had the first Under Fives turn-out back in the early 80s and within a couple of years no self-respecting club didn't have their own version of the ground-breaking Hammers firm.

The young Hammers loons came about after two twins, Billy and Toby Spanner became disillusioned with the top boys over in Pie'n'mashville constantly knocking them back when they wanted a piece of the action. So they got together a few pals and ritually burned their Panini sticker albums, tossed aside their autograph books and became Britain's youngest hooligan gang. Within no time at all, they had carved out a reputation as being a nasty bunch of lads who would cause chaos and mayhem in the name of their club and give the OB and their rivals major headaches as they tried to contain assaults from two mobs rather than the usual one. One of their early little ploys was to arrive at grounds dressed as ball boys, blag their way into the ground with some spurious story or other and then find and batter the legitimate ball collectors from wherever they happened to be on that particular away day. As the devastating attacks took place, with OB and stewards caught out by their snide little operation, they would be greeted with huge cheers from the massed ranks of travelling Hammers in the stands who would sing as one, "Run for your lives, it's the Under Fives" to the tune of Queen's Bohemian Rhapsody. The Under Fives were soon fully accepted by West Ham's ICF boys and would be allowed to bring up the rear in major offs, often carrying weapons, lunchbox-es and newspapers for the older boys.

The brothers, Billy and Toby, went on to become the infamous "Toolbox Twins" – after some bright spark had sussed they were Spanners running with the Hammers and would never leave home without Stanley knives and tape measure and the name was coined. The TTs ran large parts of the East End through sheer fear but would always look after one of their own. Neither of them lasted long once the OB recognised they were running major criminal gangs throughout the capital. They were given three options. Get nicked if they continued; start sharing their booty with bent coppers or leave the country. Billy, who was rumoured to be gay although not with his brother, fled to Canada and now works as a sous chef in Ottawa while Toby rents holiday villas in Sri Lanka. A lot of Hammers fans got a blast from the past after the devastating

Tsunami hit the former Ceylon and one of the first ex-pats to be interviewed by Sky's news team was Toby. There he was in an "Alan Devonshire...what an Iron" T-shirt doing a reasonable job of pleading for aid and describing how the giant waves had affected the area. Little did these Sky bods who beamed the pictures and interview back to Britain know they were talking to a major hood and a leading face over at West Ham during his day. Anyway, our lot only ever came up against the original Under Fives on one occasion after a visit to the happy Hammers for a Boxing Day game. What with Christmas and all, we were short on numbers and the usual choice of coach travel had to be abandoned for a more modest mini-bus. Still, we had 15 hardcore lads. Blokes who were so committed to the cause they had given up Boxing Day with their friends and family and done one to West Ham with a load of other Herberts looking to show face on the manor. We parked quite near the Queens wine bar but swerved it after seeing a couple of likely lads swapping presents belatedly outside. Farther on we came to The Boleyn and marched in bold as brass sure we would get a little tickle from the welcoming committee. It was a strategy that would accomplish the only two things we could hope for given the paucity of main players on this one. If it went off we'd probably get a couple of slaps and get put into the ground by the OB but could get our laptops out once in the away section and big it up on the hoolie websites that we'd just taken over the ICF's main boozer. Result and a huge saving of face; or we'd get a walkover from their boys and be allowed to drink some ale and join the traditional knees-up with the pearly kings and queens who regularly attend Hammers matches. It was tense as we bowled in and I was first up at the bar: "Gin and slimline tonic, if you please," I asked when I got the attention of the buxom, though bald, barmaid behind the jump. "Sorry, luv, home fans only," came the reply that left me startled. They were fuckin' sharp over here...how the fuck had she rumbled me in two minutes flat? I looked round and our lot seemed nervous. I came back with: "What, deny a visitor a drink, and this being the festive period and what not, me darling" trying desperately to disguise my own accent and at the same time not appear too condescending with my imitation of the local dialect. The bald bird with heavy breasts looked at me, gave me a cheeky smile and said: "Slimline, you say?" We were in. There was no sign of any of their top boys and we stayed until five minutes before kick-off, joined in with the Cockney hilarity and even stood a few rounds for some gnarled fogies playing the spoons in between dominoes in the corner. What a touch. One over the ICF. Nice one. Wrong. No sooner had we piled out of the boozer than we were confronted with a snarling firm of about 100 boys...and I mean BOYS. These were the Under Fives and they looked younger. Much younger. I gestured to the kid at the front who appeared to be top boy in their lot with two fingers over my nose. He was a baby, no more than eight years of age, but was already up to scratch in what is known as The Fingers, otherwise accepted as hoolie tic-tac. This system of hand gestures can come in bloody handy when there is OB crawling all over the place and I could see a couple of meat wagons out of the corner of my eye. My signal was clear and concise. It meant, "leave it out there are loads of you and you're not that grown-up, save it until you are a little older". He may have understood but Baby Bollocks was having none of it. He cradled his fingers into a church and I knew then it could get nasty. The church means, "It's your burial" but I still thought there was time to salvage the situation and came back with my right palm to my left hip: "It's a bit awkward at the minute." There was a stand off during which time I scoured these urchins to get a steer on what they had out. Fair play, they had the numbers but there was some crying at the back of their mob and it was evident that they actually had babies in prams at the rear. I'd heard of Leicester's tasty Baby Squad but this was taking the piss. Just as in the old days of pre-war football when the stands were packed and kids were passed to the front, so a couple of tiny Under Fives were passed over heads to the front of this mob so they could see better and get a taste of their first violence at football. A couple in the middle of their firm started throwing missiles and a water pistol just missed me. We stood and then, just as it looked like the OB were going to move in, the top kid raised his hand to his nose and made a flushing the pan signal. It was over and they were guaranteeing us safe passage to the visitors' enclosure as they had been impressed by the fact that at least we had turned up on what was, admittedly, a freezing afternoon. We lost 1-0 to a last-minute Marco Boogers goal that day but the abiding memory is of an off that never was and that during the whole stand off not one word had been spoken. Later that year West Ham were fined £100,000 by the FA after it was discovered club officials were in league with the ICF and had set up their own nurseries to find talent for the Under Fives. The appalling situation only emerged when one young mum left her baby son in a crèche while she attended a game and when she returned to collect him found him sitting in front of an OB video of an ICF ruck with Bristol City at Paddington one year. An embarrassed nursery worker switched the telly off but the authorities were called and the set-up busted. We don't mind starting 'em young at United but we all thought this was bang out of order.

Of course, the West Ham tiny terrors may well have been the first but they were soon copied and, some would argue, bettered.

Portsmouth's young firm failed to get off the ground despite a couple of bold efforts to recruit nippers up for the grunt. They started off with a very cute name, The House of Burberry, but fashion changes so quickly that there was a lot of in-fighting about the name they should go under. They messed around with the names, dabbled with The Church of Cerrutti 1880, tried the Stone Island Select and towards the end when standards had dropped to a low point were known as the Matalan Main Mob. Fact is lads, you can't beat the name Under Fives, really. And that's feet. Not years. Or is it?

If it's not nippers. It's birds. That's right Dorises on the bounce, looking for the off. I can't even get used to women playing football. What a laugh. Marianne Spacey? Yeah right. Hope Powell? Nah, don't think so, pal. Ladies playing football? You can keep it, mate. What a lot of nonsense that is. A bunch of girls, more often than not lesbians only in the team so they can meet new chicks, bombing about on a full-size pitch making arses of themselves. They even show it on national television now. Laughable. Makes the local Sunday League division 12 football I played in for years seem like the Premiership. And so it goes off the pitch, too. I'm afraid to report that the so-called fairer sex have never really competed when it comes to a bit of knuckle at the game. Still, they can't be good at everything and I ain't even going to try to compete with knitting, washing and pegging out wet bedsheets. No, stop it. I shouldn't. Sure there has been the odd battle which has attracted a bit of media attention, a two-minute slot on Day to Day and maybe an essay from some over-educated university plum earning a few quid from the Sunday Express for his take on this "worrying, disturbing and escalating new trend". I nearly choked on my banana chips coated in honey and served with porridge the particular Sunday morning I saw that pile of shite glaring out from my old mother's copy of the paper. I'll never forget the headline: "Terrace Hellcats". How long ago were we deprived of terraces anyway? Yet still they trot out all this garbage. This feature, written by a certain Dr. Max Burton, was accompanied by a picture of a crop-haired, snarling "bovver bird" but I suspect the picture library had no luck digging up an image of any such thing and resorted to a grainy old picture from one of those old bruisers who used to hang about in the Greenham Common Women's Peace Camp. Now if they were a firm and had they attached themselves to someone like Reading they could have caused a lot of damage. This article went on to "reveal" that alongside every proper geezers' firm in the land, is a fully committed band of women eager to go to war in the name of their club. I'm sorry, Doc, but that is bollocks. And I think you know it. In fact, I'm certain you do. But just bank the cheque, eh? To my knowledge, and the other lads I run with I might add, there are just six proper all-girl turn-outs in the whole of Britain and one of them is in the Isle of Man so they rarely get the chance to show what they're made of.

This handy little mob are known as the Natty Crew because of their impeccable style and attention to detail when it comes to dressing for the match. The girls follow Douglas Royals in the island's capital and in the pubs and bars there you can still find an old stager nursing a pint who will tell you about the time the Natty Crew missed the chance to turn out against a nasty bunch of Bishop Auckland girls who pitched up for a Woman's Own Floodlight Cup game. The Bish-Bosh, as they were known, had taunted the NC on internet hooligan messageboards and genuinely thought they had a meet arranged. But the NC weren't about when they stepped off the ferry with a "Come on then, let's be having you" call, followed, menacingly by "where are you?", I'll tell you where they were, ladies. They had all gone down to the smoke on a coach to the London Fashion Week. That's how important the right hooligan chic was to them! Incidentally, the Bish-Bosh's war cry that day lived on and became something of a legendary girlie football chant. So much so that a certain Delia Smith, celebrity chef and owner of Norwich City famously went on to coin it for herself in a well-publicised half-time rant at the Carrow Road faithful. More of Delia elsewhere though. No, as far as I am aware the NC have only ever had two meets with opposing bitch firms. Once back in 1992 when Elgin City turned up for a friendly with a car load of dykes who came up with an improvised firm and gave it a go only to get legged after three minutes of the first-half. The other was away from football at a Spring Fair when their leader, Rosie "acid-tongue" Tinker saw her home-made jam sponge fail to get even a place in the "best in show" competition while The Douglas WI took one, two and three. The tale goes that Rosie, also known as Tinkerbelle, for obvious reasons, lost it and fronted the WI leader backed by about 10 of her top girls. And when the WIs grouped together with a show of strength it was obvious it was going to kick off. A jar of sweet chutney came over the top from the WIs and that was it. A skirmish turned into a mass brawl and the NC very nearly came unstuck but, after a good two-minute ruck, the battered, beaten and bruised WI members retreated to the First Aid tent to receive treatment along with a hot cup of tea and some home-made short bread. It wasn't pretty stuff. On the floor, kicked about with the debris of battle lay three broken glasses chains, a cigarette holder and a torn headscarf. It had been brutal.

On a lighter note one of the other bitch crews who made an impression in the late 80s was a useful little gang of geezerbirds who followed AFC Sunderland and were all magicians and went by the name of Hocus Pocus Rokerites.

I once had the pleasure of sharing a train carriage with a Doris named Sammie Chung, no relation to the former Chinese manager of Wolves of the same name – after we played a testimonial up there – and she was happy to share my Tesco bag full of cold Stella with me as she recounted the bizarre circumstances which led to Sunderland having the first ladies crew in the North East. Although Newcastle would later claim they, in fact, founded Toon Tottie Troop three days before, this was subsequently proved to be bullshit and the TTT secretary, Beth Cartwright, resigned in shame after admitting doctoring the records of the mob's inception. Radio DJ Nicky Campbell had revealed this falsehood on his morning show and by the time his annoying Jock twang belted out on the airwaves the next morning, Beth had gone.

The HPR all came about when a magician called Ali Kazam (real name Richard Kazam) tried to increase business for his night classes teaching beginners magic tricks with a view to starting their own businesses catering for the increased demand for magicians at kids' parties. But, unaware of the double meaning, Ali worded the ad "Turn Tricks and Earn Extra Cash" and ran it for a week in the Sunderland Echo – and the response was a lot better than he had imagined. Sammie came clean and said she was hard-up, had just split up with her boyfriend, liked an ale or two and was keen to start a new career. "I knew what it was all about," she told me in between long gulps from her lager can, emblazoned with "12.5 percent extra FREE".

"But I had quite a fit body back in those days, didn't mind a shag or two so I thought, 'why not make a few bob on the side, like'." She wasn't alone in thinking the ad was looking for potential hookers.

Inevitably, I suppose, in the depressed North East a few bored housewives saw this as a way out of a hard, impoverished life and considered selling their bodies in the world's oldest profession. And so it was that a group of about 20 women met on a Thursday night in August at the British Rail Staff Association HQ's back room, where Ali conducted his classes, just over the road from Roker Park. They had enrolled expecting to be versed in street walking, working in massage parlours or setting themselves up from a parlour at home but instead were met with Ali, dressed in a spangly cape and sparkly hat, pointing his magic wand at each of them in turn asking them for their names. To a woman, none of them dare admit they didn't realise this was what it was all about and they got on with the tasks at hand: a few simple card tricks, and some basic slight-of-hand magic. "At first we were all sheepish about why we were there. And by the time we started to admit to each other we had all made a mistake we had grown into quite a tight-knit group. We had bonded," Sammie told me.

Over the following weeks the girls became bored with Ali and his box of tricks and, while retaining their newly found skills, started turning their attention to the forthcoming football season. "Ali turned out to be a right pervy bastard after eventually cottoning on to the real reason we had all enrolled in the first place and was trying his luck with a few of us. We were all virtually as good as him by this time and one or two of us were even making some money with shows and the like. But you couldn't help but pay attention to what was starting to happen over at Roker Park with the football season on its way."

They'd seen the coming and goings at the ground as players, fans and backroom staff prepared for first the pre-season friendlies and then the league campaign and had become more and more inquisitive.

"There was a real buzz about the place. None of us girls had ever shown much interest in football, apart from maybe drooling over their muscley legs in shorts on Match of the Day after a few bevvies indoors and a kebab on a Saturday night. But that was as far as it went. We'd all had boyfriends who were obsessed with football and

Sunderland but we were never taken to matches and actually saw football as divisive. It was something just for them and our relationships suffered because of it," Sammie continued. "Now we had a chance to be a part of it. To see what all the fuss was about. Pretty soon, we knew exactly why they were daft on football. But we never imagined with a few short weeks we would be well up for it, game as, at the match, like."

In pre-season games, Benfica, Ipswich and Coventry had all visited Roker Park and the girls had encountered a bit of an off with some Portuguese who were taking the piss out of their capes. "It was no more than a little off and we chased them into the away end before some coppers saw us off but the adrenaline rush was exceptional and we were hooked."

Sunderland's curtain-raiser was against Barnsley and the girls met in the Seaburn Arms just across from the main railway station at noon. "We got a few strange looks from the regulars that day. Well, when had they ever seen a mob of girls with magic wands, our trademark, supping white wine spritzers like they were going out of fashion? Some of Sunderland's main faces came over for a chat and we told them what we were about and that if Barnsley had a female firm we would have it with them, no problem. They were quite sweet about it in the end and after buying us a round of drinks and some ready-salted peanuts they said they had decided to accept us for what we were but that the message was, 'You can tag along, but stay at the back'.

"A couple of the girls also fixed up dates with our top boys for later in the week so we were doing rather better than we could ever have hoped. We had reckoned on maybe Barnsley turning up. First game of the season, expectation and all that and, turn up they did."

Back then Barnsley were going through a period of transition as far as their firm was concerned. They had lost a good few of top boys in the purges by the local OB. They'd had one to many tussles with away fans outside the grounds and plod had all the CCTV evidence they needed, they claimed. Dawn raids, court cases and a lot of media coverage later and half a dozen Inter City Tykes were banged up serving between six months and 18 months. It was later proved the police case was a fit-up and that the fights shown in open court to help convince these boys was actually taken on one of the hooligan OB's own video camera, in the police compound and acted out between off-duty coppers. Then they had super-imposed mugshots of the top boys onto the stars of this little pantomime and Bob's your fucking uncle. Fucking liberty-takers. The OB involved got off relatively lightly. A few early retirements with pensions intact saw them all right. As for those nicked and banged up, there was a few quid in it for them. Compo all round three years later but that didn't help Barnsley's finest when it came to making up the numbers on an away day at Sunderland. As so often has been the case with the club itself, Barnsley needed urgent help, rescuing from going out of business altogether even. Those lads who were left were up against it and a chance meeting in a chip shop in the town with local publican Derek Dibner led to one of the most unlikely of scenarios in the history of hooliganism in this old country they sometimes call Blighty. Derek was a cousin of famous steeplejack Fred Dibner, who, it was said, had fallen out with the lads who follow Bolton, his home town club. He was missing the old buzz of scrapping at football and had mentioned he was available most Saturdays for duty. It didn't matter to Fred that it was in the name of a team from a rival county, as long as he got to run with a crew and got his fix. And so it was that television personality and very good climber Fred was invited to front up the Inter City Tykes during their period of need, with a proviso that he would relinquish his duties as and when the main faces came out of the clink. Fred had readily agreed and had even rented a room above Derek's pub, a boozer which was a shrine to campanology which doubled as a disco boozer come the weekend. Derek was a known poof who hated football but was a talented local bellringer and when he wasn't at the bar of The Black Goat – known locally as Del's Bells – he could be found up the road at St Martin's knocking a few out. Tunes that is. With Fred now temporarily fronting the ICT, Barnsley's boys were back in the mood. Confidence had been low what with all the nickings but Fred soon turned things around after a couple of major results. The first was against Southend down at Roots Hall when about 25 of them steamed the main stand, scattering their youth firm, Southend Wee Ones. The second and rather more impressive show of muscle came when they had a firm's social night out down in Sheffield. Numbering 45 in total, the Tykes got cabs the short distance along the M1 to the steel city for what was to be a bit of fun, a chance to let their hair down and sink a few ales by way of bonding with Fred. To any self-respecting hoolie, it was a reasonable turnout for a wet Wednesday in Yorkshire. Come the end of the night, they were only too pleased they had travelled in such numbers. The boys had managed to get their hands on tickets for the Phil 'The Power' Taylor's short-lived forays into a new idea he had thought up with Soccer AM's blonde bombshell presenter and Torquay United supporter Helen Chamberlain. The old school pals had come up with a game that they called DartSnook, an amal-gamation of darts and snooker and had been touring the country playing exhibition games with some of the leading exponents of both sports, admittedly to mixed reviews from critics and mixed reactions from what were initially sell-out crowds. It was billed as "Where bullseye meets the baize" and Phil had managed to per-suade former host of the darts TV gameshow Jim Bowen to front the roadshow. He had also taken on Big Cliff Lazarenko, Jocky Wilson, Steve Davis, Ray Reardon and Alex 'Hurricane' Higgins. The Tykes headed for Flares, a 70s bar in the centre of Sheffield and Stella was buy-six-get-six-free. They tucked into the super-strength lager as if it were going out of fashion. By the time they handed over their tickets at the Crucible for the 9pm start, they were hammered.

DartSnook had got the attention of a fearsome mob of Sheffield Wednesday and they were in and drinking aggressively. Within 20 minutes of Jocky Wilson seeing off a brave effort from Steve Davis with a superb treble red, the taunting had started. The pissed-up Wednesdayites started singing "Dibner, Dibner, wash your face" and a few at the back of their mob hurled their inflatable dartballs. Fred saw that it was going to kick-off one way or another and decided to get in early. He slipped off his hobnail boots and crept around the back of the Crucible and scattered the Wednesday mob from behind with about 10 of his main firm. Wednesday panicked and ran, only to find their path blocked by the other Barnsley. At this point, Bowen tried to calm the two mobs with a couple of one-liners and a phrase or two from Bully. But, when tension is high, "stay out of the black and in the red, you get nothing in this game for two in a bed" doesn't cut the mustard. Nice try though, Jim. Big Jez seized the moment during the confusion and picked up Alex 'Hurricane' Higgins from the floor and hurled him into the Wednesday lot. Fists, boots and some actual dartballs did the damage and within just a few minutes the Owls had fled. Fred congratulated his firm on their victory and they all celebrated with a curry and more beer. It had been a good night.

This helped Fred to be accepted at face value at first but after a while there were one or two complaints from a couple of long-standing members of the firm. They weren't entirely happy when Fred imposed a dress code for the Tykes after a fashion disaster at home to Rotherham. "Fred was fuming when we met at the Goat at noon for the Rotherham game," remembers ICT old school hoolie Aubrey Shadwell. "Some of us were in donkey jackets with Doc Marten boots while the younger lot had Fila tracksuit tops and Lois jeans with some Nike trainers. It was a total fuck-up but there was still no need for Fred to come down so heavily on us, like."

Come down heavily on them Fred did, though and the following week when the lads met up at Barnsley railway station for the trip to Plymouth there was no mistaking they were as one. To a man they wore oil-stained blue dungarees, hobnail boots and flat caps. There faces were caked in a soot-like substance and it was clear that Fred had created a firm in his own image. The Barnsley lads were too weak, beaten and downcast after the hassle with the law. They didn't have the bollocks to challenge Fred's demands and they were to dress like this for another two seasons. To this day many of the firm who were in Fred's mob won't talk about the period. You can't blame them I suppose but you can't deny it, either, lads. You looked like right twats.

And so it was a bunch of hoolies dressed as steeplejacks stepped out at Sunderland that day looking for an off.

"About 40 of them came out of the station and tried to get in the boozer, like," according to Sammie. "Big mistake. Bouncers told them it was home fans only and they bowled off to the Dog and Duck along the road. But our lot had the scent by then. Glasses were being emptied as they spilled into the street. We weren't far behind them and would have been nearer if Sue the Flask hadn't needed to pay a visit to the ladies for a quick change down below and to freshen up. You can't go into a row if you're not dry, can you?"

Sammie went on to explain that Sunderland had fronted Fred and the boys as they left the Dog and Duck to make their way to the ground and a skirmish led to the home hoods scattering the steeplejacks to every corner. The majority of them got a fearful battering but a few, Fred included, escaped by scaling a nearby power station. When the OB arrived things calmed down and Fred and the lads even persuaded the rozzers that they were nothing to do with the off and were merely working to make the tower safe. Sammie and her Hocus Pocus Rokerites played their part in the rout of Barnsley and they built on their reputation and were voted Best Bitch Firm at the 1998 Hoolies at London's Dorchester. Sammie no longer runs with the firm by the way and works as a magician on Wearside. That's magic, Sammie!

# CHAPTER SEVEN

# Celebs, plebs, ballet and beatings

MOST lads in a firm are from the same background. Let's face it, none of us are going to become brain surgeons or rocket scientists, although Professor Roland Robinson, one of the fellas who worked for NASA did run with the Stoke lads in the late 70s. But I reckon he's the exception that proves the rule.

No, most of us are working class lads with no airs and graces, we like a good drink, a ruck and a session in the sack with a bird. Nothing wrong with that. Occasionally, and this is something the media love to make a big deal of, you get a stock-broker or someone who works in the City getting nicked by the OB. The papers go mad for it, making out that the country's going to the dogs, analysing just why someone who earns a shed load of money a week should want to get involved with something as abhorrent as football hooliganism. My answer's always the same. It's the buzz. Pure and simple.

Yeah, yeah, yeah, you may well be a mover and a shaker in some poncey office, spending the afternoon across your desk shagging your secretary, making a shed load of money and driving around in a Ferrari. But where's the buzz?

What makes you feel you're alive? Saturday afternoon when you're toe to toe with some mad ugly mob that want to tear your head off. There's the buzz my old mate. And that's just why we lads, and these solicitors, money dealers and these noncey, white collar boys love it. The buzz.

Yeah, you'll find that most lads, even if they're worth a bundle or got the arse hanging out of their jeans are basically, underneath it all, the same.

But what has changed over the past few years is the rise of the celebrity hooligan. These are the characters who have put out books describing their various exploits, sold a few copies, got a bit of notoriety and suddenly start cropping up on TV and radio telling anyone who'll listen about firms and top boys. What tends to happen is the media luvvies all come out of the woodwork and invite these lads to gallery openings, book launches and stuff like that. These lads are looked on as a bit of rough, someone from the street, and they seldom disappoint. They'll knock back the free Champagne, drink from the finger bowl, use the fish knife with the game course, then have a ruck with the maitre de, all to the great amusement of their hosts and their poncey guests. But things change, and these lads find the invitations dry up as the next oddball dinner guest arrives on the scene; an East End gangster fresh out of the nick, someone like that.

Six months later, after these lads had pissed what money they made from their five minutes of fame against the wall, they're back on the building site, never to be seen or heard of again.

But there are a couple of lads who have moved on from the hoolie world and broken in to the media big time. I'm talking of course about Terry Fenton and Mick Sweeney, or Fen-Swey as they are now known.

Fair play to these two, in 1992 they wrote one of the first serious hoolie books, *I'll Kick Your Fucking Head In*, it was published during the same week Nick Hornby's *Fever Pitch* hit the bookshops and couldn't have been more different.

Hornby's book was immediately taken to heart by the litterati, his middle class, home counties university-type personality was unthreatening and media friendly. Old Nick said all the right things and was championed as some kind of super-fan. All soft and cuddly, Hornby was football-lite.

Fenton and Sweeney were the very antithesis of him. The media took one look at IKYFHI, turned and fled. But that didn't stop them.

The book sold like hotcakes, hitting the spot with thousands of lads throughout the country, bookstores, who were initially sniffy about stocking it, soon changed their mind as they were inundated by this new book-buying section of the public.

Likewise the media were won over, and sure enough Fenton and Sweeney became regulars on BBC Radio 4's Start The Week and Channel 4's Media Show. Their honest, straight-talking views on the subjects of the day became compulsive viewing and listening. Despite, or maybe because of, the occasional lapse (for instance Fenton appeared in court for a well-publicised fist fight with Rabbi Lionel Blue prior to the UK's No.1 Hebrew lad's appearance on Thought For The Day) Fenton and Sweeney's reputation grew. In 1994 Channel 4 Films commissioned IKYFHI with Gary Oldman, Tim Roth and Melvin Hayes in the leading roles.

The film was an instant success winning The Palme d'Or at the 1995 Cannes Film Festival, and introducing the authors to a whole new audience.

The following year Fenton and Sweeney hosted ITV's late night Euro 96 show, proving that they possessed a keen and knowledge-able eye as each night they interviewed players, coaches and jour-nalists on the events of the tournament.

On the night of the final, at the end of the last show Fenton announced that he and Sweeney were moving away from football as they felt they "had given their very soul and being to the beauti-ful game, but it was time to move on". Observers noted that both wore cravats.

At the end of 1996, now using the name Fen-Swey, they debuted their new ballet Human Computer.

*From The Guardian: 12.12.96.*

*Human Computer: Saddlers Wells.*

*Review by Margaret Holland-Pryce.*

*I'll Kick Your Fucking Head In. No, not a threat or promise, but the title of the best-selling book by Terry Fenton and Mick Sweeney, aka Fen-Swey.*

*No, I hadn't heard of it either. But I am told this book has sold more* than 250,000 copies worldwide and propelled its authors into media land.

Indeed, my eldest daughter India was so excited I was to be at the press night of this ballet she implored me to attempt to gain their autographs. "They're great," she gushed. "So real". Indeed.

Writing a book with such a title is one thing, creating a work of enough merit to appear on perhaps London's most prestigious stage is quite another.

So, it was with not a little trepidation that I took my seat last night.

There had been no press pack, no preview material, just rumours of what Human Computer was to be. Stories of walkouts and stormy rows during rehearsals with choreographer Montgomery Flank being hospitalised with a broken jaw increased the tension, and I have to admit, not since I reviewed Frank Bruno's interpretation of James Joyce's Finnegan's Wake have I entered a theatre with such an open mind. I do not have to remind you that Bruno's Joycean project lasted just two performances.

There was no pre-show music, and just a white table with no chairs on the stage. Then, as a bell rang two masked figures dressed head to foot in black stepped onto the stage. From then on, we, the lucky ones who were inside the theatre were transported to a magical world, where the purest form of dance proved that art in this country is not dead. The music, a potent mixture of Burundi drumming and Celtic sea-shanties assaulted my audio senses with a cocktail so original and so vibrant, I had to grip my seat to prevent myself from screaming: "The creators of this piece are geniuses."

Naomi Curtland-Wade and newcomer Damisi Maamumi, who this time last year was shining shoes at Dar-Es Salaam bus station, gave perhaps the most important performance of modern dance this city has ever seen. One moment I was in tears, the very next I wanted to embrace the rest of the audience. There is only one problem with Human Computer, it ends.

Beg, borrow, steal...do anything to get a ticket.

The day after this review appeared the entire two-week run was sold out, touts were asking and getting £500 for a pair of tickets, Fen-Swey-mania had struck.

The two men behind Human Computer were not slow to move on once again. In the summer of 1998 at the behest of Steven Spielberg they flew to Los Angeles to discuss the making of a major motion picture. The meetings went well until, at the Belle-Vista restaurant in Venice Beach, Fenton was approached by a Leeds fan holidaying in California, and asked to sign his copy of IKYFHI.

Witnesses at the ensuing trial held six weeks later told the judge and jury that initially Fenton claimed he knew nothing of the book, telling the Yorkshireman he had made a mistake. But the fan, Anthony Parker, was not convinced and continued in his attempt to get his book signed. It was then that, as Parker told Judge Walter Nunez, Fenton threw a "tizzy poncey fit, pushed me over the dessert trolley and then burst into tears".

Parker, a veteran of many Leeds United disturbances, was not the kind of man who took being thrown into a number of bowls of tiramisu lightly, and he leapt up to seek vengeance, but instead of being ready for a toe-to—toe sort out, Fenton was quivering in the corner of the restaurant clearly unable and unwilling to defend himself. Parker, a self-confessed football hooligan with a number of police convictions behind him was still a man of honour, and simply shouted to Fenton that he had turned into a "Silly little L.A queen".

Alerted by this, Spielberg and Sweeney came to Fenton's assistance, and it was the creator of ET who now crossed swords with Parker. The Leeds fan, covered from head to foot in a variety of confections took exception to the Hollywood director's hectoring manner, and grabbed him in a headlock before bundling him through the wing doors into the kitchen where Sweeney and Bernard Millicent, the Belle-Vista security man joined in the melee. There the altercation continued causing many thousands of dollars' worth of damage both to foodstuffs and kitchen equipment. Within just a few minutes four LAPD patrol cars had arrived, quickly followed by a dozen members of the paparazzi, a TV crew from Channel 16, Dorothy Malovitz, the gossip columnist from the LA Times, Ruben Bloomstein, senior partner from Bloomstein and

Ketvitz, LA's leading firm of show business lawyers and a truck full of immigration officials who stormed into the kitchen immediately arresting the entire Belle-Vista cooking and waiting staff.

Within minutes news of the fracas was worldwide news. TV and radio shows were interrupted, newspaper front pages pulled and replaced with details of this remarkable occurrence. The British media, sensing that this was perhaps the show business story of the decade flew to LA in their droves. By 1am West Coast time, all flights from London to Los Angeles International were booked solid.

The next morning LAPD spokesperson Karen O'Brien, a fourth generation police woman, stood on the steps of Los Angeles Central Police House to make an official statement to the assembled world's press.

"Last evening an incident took place at the Belle-Vista restaurant in Venice Beach which resulted in the arrest of the following gentlemen. Mr Steven Spielberg, Mr Terence Fenton, Mr Michael Sweeney and Mr Anthony Parker. All four have been charged, under California State Law, with the following misdemeanours:

1    Acting in a manner likely to cause distress and indigestion to fellow diners.

2    Behaving in a brutish and somewhat confusing fashion.

3    Acting the goat in a public area.

All four men will be released on bail later today, and instructed to appear before Los Angeles City Court at a date to be confirmed."

It was the last charge that potentially could mean a prison sentence for all four defendants. The State Attorney's office could quite easily have sought a charge of horsing around in a public eating area and if found guilty for this, the maximum punishment was a $1000 fine, but no, he went for the more serious goat option, where a minimum of three years in a state penitentiary was more than possible.

Spielberg, keen to distance from himself from the three Englishmen, appeared on The Larry King Show the following evening, and in an emotional interview gave his side of the story. He said he was totally unaware of the hooligan background of Fenton and Sweeney, he had been under the impression Fen-Swey were theatre people, had "simply adored" Human Computer, and had been in talks with the pair with the view of taking the ballet to the silver screen. "I felt the time was right for me to express my artistic thoughts and beliefs through the power of dance. For me, and I sincerely believed Terence and Michael were of the same persuasion, there is nothing more potent in the world of art than dance. Dance is great, don't you think?"

Parker, already wanted by Yorkshire police for a string of football-related offences and yet to answer to a charge of horsing around in Leeds city centre, seemed to disappear into thin air. Skipping bail, the FBI traced him to Mexico and then Argentina though the trail then went cold. Anthony, if you're reading this my old son, use your loaf mate, turn yourself in. You can't spend the rest of your life looking over your shoulder. Stand up, be a man and do your bird.

Fenton and Sweeney retreated to their home in the Hollywood hills, their behaviour becoming increasingly eccentric and unpredictable. Both became disciples of the LA new-age guru Martha Kruypt. Kruypt was a Czech immigrant who had arrived on the West Coast in the mid 1960s. She immediately immersed herself in all that San Francisco and Los Angeles could offer at the time. Free love. Experimenting with drugs. Music. In fact, she played bass guitar on the second Grateful Dead album.

Now, well into her 60s and long tired of what the cities of the West Coast could offer her, she had, in the hills looking down on San Francisco Bay set up Pissonga (freedom in Apache) a spiritual retreat for artists and creative types. And it was to Kruypt that Fenton and Sweeney turned as they awaited their appearance in court. Under Kruypt's guidance, the two Englishmen embraced every part of this new, spiritual world. They would rise as the sun did, breakfast on barley and water from the stream. Spend the morning on the old Tai-Chi, before a lunch of barley and water from the stream. The afternoon was taken up by chanting, singing and general humming, before an evening meal of barley and water from the stream. They had turned down the opportunity to engage a high-profile celebrity lawyer to defend them, instead turning to one of their fellow residents at Pissonga, Happiness Happiness, aka Susan Murray, she hailed from New York City, and like millions before her travelled west to find herself. A poet, tarot card reader and long-time Queens Park Rangers supporter, she set about her task of keeping Fen-Swey out of the pen.

A fortnight before the trial CNN were given permission to visit Pissonga to interview Fenton and Sweeney. In the month since the incident, it was clear to everyone who watched that interview that the two men had undergone many changes. Both had lost weight. "Bollocks to the Atkins, get on the old barley and water from the stream," said Sweeney.

Fenton spoke in a quiet, almost inaudible manner, occasionally using Navahoe and Cheyenne phrases. Sweeney, his head completely shaved and painted light blue spoke in tongues. Happiness explained that her clients were "exceptional individuals who sought only to make everyone in the world smile".

There indeed was much smiling at The White Horse in Bermondsey where Fenton and Sweeney were once regulars.

The day of the trial arrived, with Parker still at large, Fen-Swey and Spielberg were ushered, through a media scrum, into court.

The prosecution, led by State Attorney Robert T. Brookes II aided by the diners and security man Bernard Millicent, painted a picture of alcohol-fuelled violence. A copy of IKYFHI was shown to the jury, and a number of particularly vicious excerpts read out (if you've read the book, you'll know the story of how Fenton, Sweeney and three associates attacked the Charlton Athletic squad and the club photographer as they were posing for their team photographs prior to the 1990/91 season).

The prosecution's final sentence was: "There is no doubt in my mind your honour that these three men were acting the goat".

Spielberg's defence team numbering fourteen, and wearing numbers and their names on the backs of their jackets, made light of their client's involvement. "Would a man who created ET get involved in soccer violence?" The answer was a resounding no and Judge Nunez threw the charges against the Hollywood producer out after just twenty minutes.

It was then time for Fenton and Sweeney to take the stand. Before they did Happiness threw rose petals in the air and hummed. "Lady, quit the humming," said Judge Nunez.

The two defendants, dressed in identical white linen robes and both wearing a large crystal around their necks faced their accusers. Brookes asked them "Were you once football hooligans?" "Did you once spend your lives searching for violence?" "Have you been to Hull's new ground?"

"Yes", Yes", "No" came the reply. "We are innocent men," pleaded Sweeney. "Yes, we did once live a life that was full of hate and violence. We would travel the country seeking to spread misery and pain to others, but those days are gone. We are reborn. We are now not those men."

As Sweeney warmed to his task, Happiness picked up a set of nose flutes and accompanied his statement with a selection of South American folk tunes. "We have come to your great country, a place of freedom and peace, and it is here we want to live our lives. At Pissonga we are amongst beautiful people who share our vision. It is there we will remain, if they do something about the menu, that is. I ask the men and women of the jury to not look at us as the authors of a torrid football hooligan book, but instead as men who have woken from a sleep, and found the new day is a beautiful, sunny day."

Happiness, unable to contain herself had now switched on a ghetto blaster which pumped whale calls into the courtroom, she was in a state of near trance, her arms held up high, eyes tightly shut, she swayed, all the time moaning and chanting.

Sweeney went on: "We have great plans, your honour, we want to go to the inner cities, meet the children, and teach them about love, about caring, about the play-offs. I ask you to set we free. I ask the jury to set we free. Set we free, set we free!"

Happiness took up the chant: "Set we free", as did the Pissonga residents who sat in the public gallery.

"Set we free, set we free!"

"OK, OK enough of this" said Judge Nunez, angrily banging his gavel on his high wooden desk.

"You two are kooks, crazies, flakes. Tell that woman to turn that tape off and stop that confounded moaning. Then get your asses out of my court. Case dismissed."

Fen-Swey and Happiness stood on the steps of the courthouse and savoured their freedom.

Around them, Martha Kruypt and the Pissonga people celebrated in mime.

It was then back to their home in the hills for barley and water from the stream. For tomorrow was another day.

# CHAPTER EIGHT

# Making great strides for Africa

FOOTBALL hooligans have been castigated over the years for their exploits and any reasonable lad couldn't mount any sort of defence of what they get up to without spluttering on their Stella. Don't get me wrong: we all understand why we do it, but we don't expect the great British public to. Nor the OB, neither. But what fails to get as much coverage as a ruck in Rotherham or some capers in Coventry is the softer side of your run-of-the-mill hoolie. Over the years various firms have done a lot of good work for charity, culminating in what is now a very firmly established calendar event in the fund-raising year. Stone Island Day is the one day a year when all the nastiness is put to one side and top boys get together to have a laugh, generally make plums of themselves and raise millions of pounds for deserving causes in the process. It started as a humble little event held in 1983 in Port Talbot and brought together hoolies from Wrexham, Cardiff and Swansea's firms eager to play their part. You've got to remember that the majority of these lads have spent their lives turning their noses up at charity collections and before this new initiative wouldn't know a sponsored walk from a dip in the sea on Boxing Day. Their idea of charity would be to spare the poor sod they've just handed out a beating to from another couple of slaps and relieving him of any designer clobber. So it was that the first charity day was a little rough around the edges but, hey, these lads' hearts were in the right places...even though it was for only one day. Afan Lido FC staged the inaugural do which saw events such as the 100-yard dash (chasing imaginary away fans); Pint Glass Challenge (seeing who could hit a dummy's head from the back of the bar); Tidy Trotting (where a group of no more than 30 lads have to jog together in a tight unit as if they are either a) getting away from the OB or b) sussing out the town centre after getting off the train) and Boots Endurance (seeing how many kicks to the legs you could take before collapsing. The record set that day was 77 by Ewan "Sheephead" Thomas and it has still to be broken. He got £1 a kick from sponsors). The charity to benefit that first year was Trousers for Africa, which provided strides to those in need from Timbuktu to Tunis. In total, the lads raised £645.67 and a cheque was duly sent to the charity's HQ in Chad. Fair play, lads. Cardiff Soul Crew's Big Taffy O'Leary was the inspiration behind that first-ever event. He'd been on a drugs run to Morocco to pick up a tonne of hash in a converted camper van and was appalled to see so many locals bowling around in just their pants. Taffy, who even came up with his own slogan, Making Strides For Strides, remembers: "I thought of my kids and how they might feel going to school in just their undies, like. It made me feel very guilty and I made up my mind there and then that I wanted to do something about it. I had some spare trousers in the wardrobe at home which no longer fitted me because I've put on a fair few pounds over the years, but these wouldn't make a huge difference. We're talking about thousand of trouserless souls. I had to do something more than just donate my old strides.

"I made a couple of calls to the top lads at the other Welsh clubs and after some initial laughing and piss-taking, and a few 'fucks' and 'twats' they agreed to take part. All that is except the boys from Newport County, but they've always been a horrible lot. No offence, lads.

"At first we weren't exactly sure what to do but my old nan used to work for Oxfam and she gave us some ideas. A few of the older lads donated gear that had seen action in brawls back in the 60s and one item, a framed, blood-stained donkey jacket complete with the knife used in the attack signed by both victim and assailant fetched £210 at auction. We were on our way and the money started flooding in.

"Things got a bit messy towards the end of the day, though. Trouble is, you can't expect some of the meanest lads in Wales not to fancy a scrap after a bellyful of beer and having their enemies so close to hand. But what we did was, right, we said to the top boys, 'fair play, have it right off but we want £50 per mob'.

"They were as good as gold, mind, and the money was collected in a pint pot. We allowed each team 30 boys and got permission to let them on the pitch for 15 minutes and they kicked fuck out of each other, basically.

"Cardiff claimed they were the winners but as I said to their top, top boy, Careless Caradawg, 'hey, big man, we're all winners today and so are the children of Africa'."

A month or so down the line, Taffy received some pictures in the post from Africa and he admits they brought a tear to his eye. There, in all their glory, were a group of boys no older than 11, beaming with pride as they showed off their new trousers, complete with snake belts to hold them up. In the middle of the group, one of these poor mites held a signed photograph of Harry Secombe, which Taffy had sent as a personal donation. Zanny, the PR girl at the Cardiff Soul Crew's HQ, immediately fired off a press release to all the local rags along with a picture and it made the hoolie trade mag, The UK Lads' Gazette, and it caught the imagination of firms all over the country.

"The boys at the UKLG were really good actually and they helped us raise awareness and even donated some free advertising space," remembers Taffy. The magazine has been a huge success since it was launched by one-time Aston Villa top lad Shane Holmes back in 1992. Holmesy was forced to retire from the knuckle after a particularly brutal skirmish with some Olympiakos fans at the Acropolis while on holiday in Athens and wanted to somehow contribute to the big, bad world of football yobbery. Although Holmsey obviously wasn't too quick on his feet (he'd been the only Villa lad caught by the Greeks as they legged it down the mountain because of his lack of speed) he was quick mentally and, having always written for the Villa fanzine, A Fine Claret, decided to put this to the test. The mag which was started as a one-man band now employs more than 15 journalists reporting on every aspect of hooliganism. They sell around 60,000 a week and have a further 20 admin and ad sales staff. One of the nice things about Holmsey and his publication is that they are always willing to put something back into our world. They are not simply take take, take, like some of the more well-established mags. You know who you are, boys. One of the schemes Holmsey has in place at the UKLG offers a couple of Villa's brighter youth mob a scholarship, with qualifications and a job at the end of it on the mag. Fair, play Holmsey on that one. Diamond, mate. And so it was that he championed the Trousers for Africa cause.

And their contribution helped the cause no end and it just snowballed from there. Little did Taffy know that that small effort to help strideless Africans way back then would turn into the massive fundraiser that is the modern Stone Island Day, which comes a couple of quid behind Red Nose Day in terms of money donated to charities in Britain. Well, they haven't got Lenny Henry, have they?

The 1983 fundraiser didn't have a sponsor, of course, but Stone Island, the preferred label of choice for any right-minded hooligan, were quick to offer help. These days mobs set aside one Friday every Spring to stage wacky events throughout their communities to raise money for various causes. You can't move without seeing the famous Stone Island motif: pensioners wear pin badges: girl guides sell copies of football riot videos from actual police surveillance footage at car boots sales and even the emergency services join in (apart from the police, who to this day have failed to recognise the charity), with fire crews staging mock rescues of hoolies stuck up trees. Naturally, celebrities have been quick to jump on the bandwagon. While Bono and Bob Geldof seem to shy away from helping out, citing some other charity work they are committed to, stars such as Dame Edna Everage, Ant and Dec and Vinnie Jones have all contributed. TV stations were at first reluctant to offer a platform for the whole shooting match but eventually satellite station Bravo signed a deal to bring viewers' skits, sketches and general madcap behaviour all in the name of Stone Island Day. Comic Ricky Gervais was persuaded to come on board as was Peter Kay. The lads came close to admitting they used to run with Reading and Bolton respectively but you can forgive them for not actually coming out and admitting it. Especially on live TV. Ricky went as far as switching to his brilliant David Brent character from The Office in a talking heads piece to camera to tell viewers: "What is hooliganism? Yeah. At football matches, is there any? Is it deeper than that, though...'cos... I've been to rugby matches, yeah, and seen players trying to bite each other all over. That can't be sport. But it is. So, is...can hooliganism be quantified?" Nice one Ricky, sorry, David...and all for charity. Peter Kay recorded a version of the old hit "Hit him on the head with a baseball bat" and shot a video with a load of infamous boys carrying on in the background. It failed to chart but gave Peter the germ of an idea for another re-release just recently to raise money for Red Nose Day. Peter teamed up with crooner Tony Christie to film a video for his hit Is This The Way To Amarillo and it went down a storm. Nice one, Peter. Big fan of the Trotters is Pete. That's Bolton, not feet.

Richard Madeley, from TV's Richard and Judy Show, seems a reasonable chap but I never thought he would get involved. But he did and in quite an authentic way, bless him. I've never really had a problem with Madeley but some of our firm have never liked him ever since around the time that he was cleared in a shoplifting trial back in the early 90s. A few days before he'd called Nottingham Forest 'Notts' Forest and, in our book, even though we fucking hate Forest, that's a footballing knowledge no-no. They won the bleedin' European Cup after all. Twice. Fat chance our mob have got of landing that particular piece of silverware. LDV Trophy? Yeah, well. That's as maybe. Anyway, we all know the correct abbreviation is 'Nottm', or something like that anyway, but forgive and forget I say.

They can be a funny lot our boys, unforgiving in so many ways. "Look lads," I tried to reason in our local boozer the night after the suave presenter was acquitted of stealing wines, spirits and a box of soap powder from a Tesco supermarket. "Madeley's a bit slick and, yes, can drone on a bit. But put him up against the likes of, say, John Barnes on Channel Five's football shows and you see just how professional Madeley can be." If you are reading this Barnesy, brilliant footballer and all that but, hey, leave the telly work to the pros my old son.

"It's just not done," Skinny Jeff retorted as he manoeuvred his nicotine-stained fingers around a pack of Old Holborn, a bit of Malawi you-know-what and some Rizlas. "Madeley's dropped a clanger that my six-year-old neice wouldn't have done. I've got no time for him. Or his missus for that matter." Bit harsh on old Judy but, that's Skinny Jeff for you. He said no more and went out into the beer garden for a smoke.

But Madeley proved he was a game lad and fair play to him for that. He even went as far as dressing as a top boy and starting on some Hull City lads at King's Cross, who were down for a game at Brentford. When they started to get the better of him, well, he was on his own, he took off his baseball cap to reveal his familiar locks and ever-youthful appearance and spluttered: "You've been Madeley-ed...it's all for Stone Island Day!" The lads burst out laughing and started looking around for the hidden cameras and patting each other on the back. The footage still does the rounds on hoolie websites to this day. "I can't believe we fell for it," says one Hull lad as he dabs a cut lip with a tissue. "Still it's all for charity. Well done, Richard, you old tosser. Now how about a few pints? Oh, and get your fuckin' missus along. The blonde bird who lobs her knockers out on live TV."

Six years ago the top lads from the nation's top firms surpassed themselves to help bring emergency relief to the people of another African country, suffering at the hands of lawless, gun-toting rebels in genocide-hit Rwanda. A BBC2 documentary shot under cover showed the true extent of the killing there and once again the much-maligned hoolies got off their collective arses and actually did something about it, made a difference. Again, Big Taffy O'Leary was involved. "I saw the killing and it was just awful," Taff remembers. "One lad, obviously one of the the Tutsi-led rebel movement RPF, was begging for his life and the Hutu about to kill him gave him the wanker sign before beheading him. I'd seen something similar in a summer tour with Wales to Finland, except, there was no killing going on, just battering people, like. I knew we had to try to do something."

Hoolie Aid was launched with comic Jim Davidson fronting the whole thing. Within a few days Jim managed to get together the leading faces from all the main firms with the idea of making a record with the proceeds going to the appeal. Boy George, Lemmy from Motorhead and Annie Lennox were roped in but no one, not even Sanguine Dave and Derek, two of Hull City's main faces and the-then holders of the Stella Book of Records title of "the most over-optimistic twins following a football team," could have known just how quickly the appeal would grow.

Davidson had already enquired of his old pal Ron Noades about the possibility of staging a concert at Brentford's tidy little Griffin Park ground and when he went on Newsnight to be quizzed by Jeremy Paxman about it, he famously lost the plot in his attempt to stir the public into handing over their hard-earned wonga. "Give us your blinking money," he stormed and Paxman tried to question exactly where the funds would be placed. The Sunday Times had run a story the day before suggesting that some of the money had been diverted to an offshore account in the name of former ticket tout Fat Stan Flashman but Davidson was having none of it. "Never mind about all that just give us your blinking money, nick, nick," he ranted. His explosion, littered with a fair smattering of expletives, made every news bulletin in the land and the job had been done. Big Taffy was in the studio that night as Jim dodged the awkward questions but, for legal reasons, wouldn't go into the Flashman account. "He's a long-time dead, anyway" was all he would tell me.

Obviously bowling about with no trousers on is a desperate position to be in and fashion doesn't come into it for some of these underprivileged folk.

But fashion has always been an important part of top boys going to football. It goes right back to the 1960s, Joe Hawkins, skinheads and all that.

I remember my older brother Steve going off to games in the early 70s wearing all sorts of amazing gear. First of all there was the Fred Perry, braces, Levis and Dr Martens gear, which was the classic skinhead look.

He had the lot, and really looked the part. Friday night became something of a ritual, as I helped him get his clobber ready for Saturday afternoon. He'd get in from work, get his tea down him double quick, then nip out to the pub for a few swift pints. Back he'd come around 11 o'clock, full of beer and if I was lucky a can of something and a bag of fish and chips for me.

I've watched some of these poncey BBC2 programmes about this shirt-lifting graduate type toss-pot who pissed off to a jungle somewhere and shacked up with some fuzzy-wuzzy tribe for a few weeks. You know the score, he turns up alone, oh yeah, apart from a film crew, soundman and his make-up artist, and immerses himself into the culture of this tribe of jokers. Anyway, one of the programmes showed how they'd prepare their warriors if they felt there was about to be an off with some other tribe. Anyway, the same kind of ritual took place at our house. Steve would pick out his shirt, braces, tonic trousers, the whole lot, right down to the silk handkerchief and tie-pin for the next day.

I'd get out the ox-blood polish and give his footwear of choice a right going over.

The next morning we'd both be up early to make sure he looked the bollocks. The splash of Brut, a dab of Brylcreem, the metal comb...the whole ensemble, when put together looked great. Then off he'd go, just like one of them tribal warriors, with me his batman wishing I was old enough to go with him.

If Steve had gone off to a home game, I'd be sitting at the window waiting for him to come home with news of the knuckle, reports of the grunt. Most Saturdays he'd be back home with the programme for me, and once our parents were out of ear-shot he'd let me know how the firm had fared that afternoon. Occasionally he'd have a trophy for me. I remember him bringing me scarves he'd "taxed" from Spurs, Leeds and Derby fans. There was also a pair of lederhosen he'd relieved a Bayern Munich fan of after a UEFA Cup tie, a pair of tickets for the Eisteddfod he'd got from a Cardiff fan and a couple of Elm saplings and a fully grown Weeping Willow he and his mates had pinched off a Nottingham Forest face.

The skinhead scene eventually metamorphosised into the suedehead scene, crombies, tonics, loafers and Ben Sherman shirts. From then on it all went a bit haywire with white builders dungarees and butchers coats, high-waisted flared trousers, stack heels and budgie jackets. Perhaps the nadir for terrace fashion was in the mid 1970s. The influence of Pomp Rock was there for all to see. Football and music, both premonitory working class pursuits always seem to mirror each other. A good example is when the BBC actually get off their leftie arses, put their copies of The Guardian down and run some repeats of Top Of The Pops. Forget the groups miming to some long forgotten hit, take a look at the audience. The clothes the lads are wearing and more or less what went for fashion on the terraces at that time. The Leeds lads really took to what was happening on the music scene at the time. I distinctly remember waiting at the station to welcome Yorkshire's finest for an FA Cup tie in 1974. This was the time when Rick Wakeman was taking sartorial excess to new heights (or lows, depending on your taste). A few of us were on the platform having a quiet fag and sipping on a can or two of Skol, just waiting to see how many Leeds' top boys were making the trip south. Sure enough, the 9.20 from Leeds pulled in, the doors bursting open before the train fully stopped, and out jumped a few of the more eager lads to take a look at what was on the horizon. These fans were mostly scarfers and youth and were small beer and of no interest to us. No, we were on the lookout for the real Leeds lads, and it didn't take too long for us to clap eyes on them.

Suddenly, from one of the carriages to the rear of the train, a deafening racket almost made our ears bleed. It was the opening bars to Emerson, Lake & Palmer's version of "Fanfare For The Common Man". Our eyes were blinded by what seemed to be a pyrotechnic light show and the air was full of glitter. And out they came onto the platform, or should I say out they hobbled. None of us had ever seen the like, they had stack heels, capes, wizard's hats, the lot.

Oh yes these lads looked the business, but it only took our firm a few seconds to realise that even these boys would have fitted in nicely in the chorus line of The Rocky Horror Show but for some toe to toe action with our mob of top faces, they'd got things badly wrong.

One of their lot had got his cape trapped in the train door, and that was the signal to steam into them. What happened next would have made Marc Bolan's corkscrew hair turn grey. Seven-inch stack heels are good, no doubt, but not as good as a six-hole cherry red Dr Marten boot. The taller they are, the harder they fall they say, and when you're falling onto hard, cold British Rail tarmac from nearly seven feet, that's a long way to fall. One of their main lads had the full Aladdin Sane look, which was red and blue metallic flash across his face and a white zip up cat suit with "ELLAND ROAD" in green sequins on the back. This poor guy took on hell of a pasting and the last I saw of him he was limping out of the station, you could just make out the word "DAD" as he shuffled away.

The next big thing to happen was the Punk explosion. It really was amazing how, in just a matter of days, lads who had been coming to football with shoulder length hair, loon pants and stack heels suddenly re-invented themselves.

Our firm took to Punk big style, we had the works: safety pins, ripped jeans, biker jackets and dog collars. Suddenly, lads who had been known as Chelsea Dave or West Ham Phil wanted to be known as Dave Vortex and Belinda Wilkins. Well, perhaps West Ham Phil wasn't a particularly good example...let's just say "Belinda" is now happily married to the assistant manager of B&Q's Ilford branch, and "her" husband has no knowledge of "her" footballing past.

Anyway, Punk was a great time. We'd go to the game, have a row with the locals, then more than likely meet up with them again at a concert in the evening. Some of the more sussed bands realised that most of the lads in the audience were firm, and courted our support. Now this was a dangerous game to play and a bit like playing with fire. Soon the inevitable happened, with firms adopting bands and vice-versa. The result was you'd travel up to say, Manchester to watch your team at Maine Road, exchange a few pleasantries with the boys from the Kippax, them more than probably continue the row at a Lurkers gig. Our boys really got into The Phlegm, who were not a major league punk band, but for a few months in 1977 they were the dog's bollocks. As all the bands did back then, they went down the DIY road and recorded and released their own single. The B-side was "Get into 'Em", which was apparently inspired by our adventures on the football terraces of this fair land. Yeah, I bought a copy...why not? It's up in the loft somewhere with all my other paraphernalia from those long lost days.

# CHAPTER NINE

# Grasses, arses and my old Dad

POSH people go to the opera and the ballet. They spend a week's wages on a meal in a swanky restaurant. They try to impress their friends by going to watch some arthouse French film or waste a day looking at some bird's unmade bed in an art gallery. It's what they do.

But it's not what me and my mates do.

As I have mentioned, most boys who run with firms are ordinary working class lads who do mundane, poorly paid jobs. For them, what goes on each Saturday is what keeps them going, keeps them sane. From 9am on a Monday morning to 5pm on a Friday afternoon, their thoughts will be on the buzz of being with their mates and following their team.

Obviously, there are exceptions.

Reading had a neat little crew in the late 90s who were all butlers and footmen at Windsor Castle; The Dukes of Hazard were a vicious mob of aristocratic types, many with blue blood, some of them in direct succession to the throne who caused mayhem up and down the country following Notts County.

Perhaps the most famous were The Luton Weather Men, who were just that. These lads all worked for the Met Office, some presenting weather forecasts on the BBC. I remember running into this lot at Paddington station on the way back from Plymouth a few years back.

They were a nasty bunch and their weapons of choice were those sun and cloud icons used on the TV, sharpened up. One of those can do a lot of damage. Weather icons aren't the only weapons that can cause concern at football. It reminds me of that infamous picture of the Liverpool fan being escorted around the pitch at Old Trafford after copping a dart in the head at a particularly troublesome encounter between the two great rivals during the mid-70s. Everyone assumed this was randomly lobbed by a United yob into the Scoreboard End with any Scouser as a target. Wrong! The offending arrow was actually hurled by Ken "Bully Boy" Kennedy, a top 20 player in the pro game back then. As well as being a darts ace Ken was a diehard United fan and had been approached by a third party representing some irate Cockney Reds who were eager to get one over on one of Liverpool's top boys, Joey "Knuckles" Mackay. After a good few Boddingtons in the city centre boozers, Ken had agreed to pick out Knuckles later on that day at the match. Despite being half-cut, Ken expertly targeted Joey from his seat in the main stand. It was an awesome hit and one which gained Ken legendary status in Salford's pubs and clubs until he pegged it in a highly suspicious speedboat accident off of Selsey Bill in the summer of 1984. To this day no one has ever been brought to trial in connection with Ken's untimely death. The only witness, who described the man at the helm of the speeding vessel as "a curly-haired, moustachioed fella who screamed, 'have that, whack'," when he hit and killed Ken as he bobbed on the water on a lilo soaking up the sun.

Over the years there's been a lot in the press about how professional people such as solicitors, barristers and dentists have all joined in with football violence. There was a recent dawn raid by the OB who put the squeeze on a mob of Southampton and discovered one of their top boys was a lay preacher. Apparently he had become disillusioned with JC and searched for something new and found the exhilarating world of football hooliganism. A quick search on the internet and he discovered that there was a football team nicknamed the Saints, which meant he could get involved in the offs and not feel to badly about it as at least there was a religious link. Incidentally, this pulpit casual was spared jail after doing a deal with the prosecution to snitch on his fellow Southampton hoolies. Man of the cloth indeed.

Maybe, now and then someone like that does get involved, but I've found more often than not the average boy id mid to late twenties and working class.

The majority of these lads like their violence straight down the middle, as it comes. Others, however, have quirks. Serious ones at that. One such mob is a mean mob with a tendency to self-harm. That's right, you read it right first time sunshine. Self-harm!

The following passage is from an essay written by the eminent humanoligist and former war poet Kevin Welling. The American writer's account of his meeting with this particular group of hardcore hooligans first appeared in an edition of *Geezer* magazine in April 2000. The entire article has since been reproduced many times around the world since its first publication and has led to a clutch of awards for Welling. After a spell at *Geezer* during which time he lived in London, Welling moved back to the States where he is currently living in Los Angeles and working on "movie projects" with Hollywood star Sean Penn. We have re-produced a section of it here with kind permission from Martin King of Headhunter Publishing:

YOU could see they had been in a battle. This weary, bloodstained and dishevelled bunch traipsed across the concourse as one. A tired glance up at the train times on Euston station's giant indicator board from one of their number every five or six paces. They wore a uniform, of sorts. But these soldiers weren't part of any military exercise. Far from it. Brilliant white trainers emblazoned with motifs from sports brands such as Nike, Lacoste and Fila ferried their owners silently towards the platform that housed their transport. The train that would take them home to loved ones. It was difficult to see whether this self-fashioned army had suffered defeat or scored a victory. But they had fought hard, that wasn't in doubt, judging by their wounds and ramshackle appearance. Yet they retained an air of order,

WELL UP FOR IT!

despite their raggedy collectiveness. They may well have been battered but they were unbowed. Their uniforms picked them out amongst the regular travellers at one of London's busiest railway stations. To a man, they wore jeans, varying in shades of blue denim. Up top, it was overcoats. Stone Island, seeing as you ask. And don't forget the accessories. Burberry scarves and baseball caps. Lots of them. They had been in a battle all right. But exactly who were they and what had they been through? I was in London to find out. They were soccer hooligans of that there was little doubt. But for which soccer club did they root? Who were their enemies and what was their deal? I drained my glass of warm beer in the bar that overlooks the station and ventured down the staircase to enquire. I approached a stout, ginger-haired soldier waiting for a "double cheeseburger and chips, no salad on the burger, yeah" at the Burger King. "Hi, I'm an American writer," I said, a little nervously. "I'm here in Britain to try to make some sense of the whole soccer hooliganism thing. But, hey, don't worry. I'm writing it for *Geezer* magazine and they want me to be fair and honest in my approach. I have no preconceptions of you guys. Hey. I'm an American."

The title of the magazine acted as if it were a bullet fired into my target's brain. He jolted, and then turned his head towards me. "*Geezer*," he repeated. "You're working for *Geezer*? That's my favourite lads' mag, geezer. Do you know, or have you ever met, Brian Brain, 'the man's insane'?" He chuckled at the mantle. I hadn't but I knew of whom he spoke. Brain was a whisky-guzzling old school operator who came up from the tea boy ranks at *Geezer* to become the title's leading writer. He was brash, brazen and Brazilian. Real name Manuel De Silva. Brian Brain to a nation. "Only, he's well good," added my man in parlance I thought needed correcting but you do the math. I knew what he meant. "Yes, me and Brian share an office. We regularly go for beers together," I lied. "We were with Chelsea in Milan when we blew up that hotdog stall and blamed it on the Ultras. We ran at Olympiakos together with Man United and we sat back and watched EastEnders with Tottenham one night while Arsenal were in Europe to see what the other side felt like. Man, we do copious amounts of gear, you know?" He came back. "Nice, excellent in fact." "So," I said, "What's happened to you guys tonight, man? You've been in the wars." I remembered some useful phrases Clive the graphic artist back in the office had told me. He was a fan of Fulham. "You been done at West Ham? Legged by Palace? Run by QPR? You lot look as if you've taken a right pasting," I said nervously, quickly adding: "I'm sure Brian Brain would be interested to know." His face contorted and then the rage subsided. "Nah, mate, we're self-harmers. Leave it, eh?" He walked away. So did I.

The actual piece goes on to describe more of Welling's time in Britain observing "soccer hooligans". Later, much later, he wrote a book on his time here. *In with the Yobs* was reasonably successful but was hardly fellow American Ricky Rayner's seminal *Gone Off Big Time*. But the reason I have included the passage here is to highlight one of the firms of which very few of you will have heard. The self-harmers, who call themselves The Injury, are hardcore. Make no mistake. Some would say that most of these boys are a certificate short of being sectioned under the mental health act. I'm not one of them, though. The Injury is made up of disaffected lads from firms all over the country. Some have proved too hardcore. Others upset other firm members with their manners. Some were running with mobs who just didn't see enough action for their liking. As soon as the fixture lists come out at the end of July, these boys pick out the tastiest games all over England. They don't follow one team. They are, as Welling later wrote, "hermaphroyobs". In other words their fighting allegiances are ambiguous. They'll pitch up at Millwall-West Ham and demand that both sets of Londoners tear into them. They'll arrive at the forecourt at Old Trafford on Derby day and start on both United and City. They'll walk into the Strawberry pub outside St James' Park wearing Sunderland shirts on Derby day, take a beating or otherwise and then run around to the away fans entrance, changing into Newcastle shirts as they go. And, as a treat, once a year they'll travel up to Scotland for the Old Firm game and create merry hell by parading outside either Parkhead or Ibrox and sing a song made up with the lyrics of both The Fields of Athenry and The Sash. It provokes both sets of fans and The Injury get what they want: all out war and more often than not, a good hiding.

The sinister side of The Injury comes out when they can't find foe. That's when they turn on themselves. It doesn't happen often but if they travel to a match and for some reason it's postponed, they'll pick a fight with themselves and lay into each other. Then the self-harming kicks in and they'll branch off into various groups and start punching, kicking and cutting themselves. It's pretty sick stuff. They can end up in a right mess. As Welling found that night on Euston station.

We touched on grasses earlier when I told you about the priest who shopped the Southampton lads as part of a deal to get a reduced sentence. Sneaks, snitches call them what you like but one thing every firm has to be on guard for is informers. And, alarmingly, not all grasses come from within. Increasingly, the OB will place undercover plod in a firm and reap the rewards. Let's face it, the OB can be a crafty lot when they want to, and they will attempt to gain evidence on an operational crew by infiltrating it with one of their own.

Many recent high profile arrests and subsequent court cases have been down to top boys in a firm getting sloppy, taking their eye off the ball and not vetting new members closely enough.

The OB get in, ingratiate themselves with the main faces while all the time feeding information about the firm back to OBHQ.

With someone on the inside of a firm, the powers that be are always one step ahead of a mob. I remember our crew being infiltrated by a couple of OB in the mid 90s.

All of sudden, tasty offs that had been arranged were being cancelled. We'd arrive at a boozer miles away from the ground to find the place crawling with plod, or the day before a nice looking away day a few of us top boys would receive an early morning call from the boys in blue.

That's one tactic to put the kybosh on any knuckle actually happening. The other way, and this is what happened to us, is they let things occur, then bang, crash, wallop and your front door is caved in at 6am.

That's what can happen if your firm start to get a rep and you begin to attract interest from lads outside your immediate circle.

From the very first word written in this book, I've pledged to pen a warts-and-all account of my days with the firm, so I'm not afraid of admitting that I have made mistakes along the way. That's why I'm going to hold my hands up and admit I should have sussed our two OB grasses weeks before they stitched us up big time.

What happened should have sounded alarm bells in my little bonce but, hey, I was duped. And I wasn't the only bleeder, either. So I was none the wiser when these two lads turned up when we were on one at West Brom. No one had seen them before, but after the game they proved handy lads as they helped us give the Boing Boing boys a lesson in manners.

They came back down to London with us on the train, getting the drinks in, sharing the banter and dropping a few names.

No one thought anything of it. The next week there they were again, in the local buying drinks, talking about the off, generally making themselves useful. I have to say they were very convincing.

This went on for a couple of months, but looking back there was one night when I should have sussed them. I really did let myself down badly.

We were at home to Tottenham, always one of the many highlights of the season, when these two nonces turned up in the boozer. It had been raining heavily all day, and they both had on two long black raincoats.

I remember being somewhat taken aback when they undid their coats and both were wearing police uniforms! It later came out in court that they'd been running late and forgotten to get into their firm clothes.

Fair play to them, they noticed me giving them the eye, but simply told me after the game they were off to a fancy dress party.

So that was that. They stuck with us for a month or so, travelling up to Wolves and Man City, each time just being on the periphery of the action. Doing just enough to convince us they were the real deal.

Of course what these planks were doing was recording each and every bit of action, noting down names, places and faces.

Then, whoof: they'd gone in a puff of smoke. They were nowhere to be seen.

But we did see them again, across the court room. They had their uniforms on, but this time there was no party.

Four of us went down, another half dozen got tagged.

The Bird was no big deal, it's part and parcel of being a top boy.

I'd be lying if I said going inside for the first time didn't phase me a bit, but once you get into the swing of things, it's more like a holiday camp than a prison.

Most of the lads in clink, if not directly involved with firms, had a pretty good idea of how things worked.

I did just under three months in Aylesbury nick, which in reality was a picnic.

My main regret was I missed some top rows with Sheffield United and Millwall.

In chokey, I met a lot of top boys. Still in touch with a few of them to this day, even though they are City! One of these fellas, let's call him Para Pete, was a gem of a bloke who was doing time after seeing off three OB with a fire extinguisher during a scrap between the paras and some RAF engineers at a Grays Athletic v Hornchurch Essex Cup clash. In a word he was bloody mental. I often asked him how on earth these two regiments had come to blows at a low-key non-league game. Pete would roll his eyes to the ceiling and say: "Don't ask, pal." What I do know is that Pete had been drummed out of the paras by the time of the ruck at Grays' Recreation Ground but the half-a-dozen or so he was with were still serving Queen and country. Pete took the rap so his pals could stay in the service. That was the type of bloke he was but his loyalty meant he was doing six months. On the upside he had the benefit of my company for the duration. Pete was a great storyteller and we would often talk long into the night about the various scrapes and scraps we'd been in over the years. Somehow I always felt Pete's tales were tastier than mine and I could never seem to compete with him, especially when it came to the more unusual tales from his travels in the army. Two yarns in particular caught my imagination and, to be honest, I wasn't entirely convinced they were accurate but subsequent research I've done has led me to think they are spot on.

The first I shall repeat here concerns England's biggest footballing enemies other than Scotland and Germany...Argentina.

This bunch of beef-eating cowboys done themselves no favours in the Falklands and actually lost plenty of top boys in the Battle for Goose Green back in 1982. The Paras slotted no end of Argies in that little dispute but their job would have been made more difficult had there not been divisions within the ranks of the South Americans. River Plate's mob, Inter-Pampas Amigos, refused to fight alongside their Buenos Aires rivals from Boca Juniors, The Little Perishers. Before General Galtieri issued the order to invade the Malvinas Islands, Falklands to you and I, he invited the ace faces of the two firms to a meeting at his presidential palace in the capital. The crux of the meeting was this: Would the two hated rivals, who for years had beaten shit out of each other in the name of football honour, come together as one in a new regiment to take on the British forces. The answer was a resounding 'No'. These two HATED each other after all. Carlos the Smack-all, so named, said Pete, for his ability to wade in with fists and down as many as 40 rivals a minute at the front of the Perishers, even went as far as to attend the meeting in a diving suit complete with oxygen tank because, in his words, "I don't want to chance breathing in air that might have circulated in the lungs of the devil". The 'devil' Carlos was referring to was the IPA's very own Jose Antonio Sunbeam and he probably deserved the mantle more than any hooligan ever. (Apart from Leigh RMI's Insane Chris, possibly, but more of him later). He was what any clued-up south Bermondsey boy would call a top growler. But Jose was in no way a conventional thug, far from it. He was a piano tuner by trade and had studied at the city's Institute of Fine Art. His interest in the Fallen Angel was legendary and he even claimed on a local radio show that he not only met Beelzebub, but had got a signed shirt as well. Anyway, it falls to General Galtieri to cut the meeting short to sign another half dozen death warrants and the two men who could have changed the course of history, had they been willing to get together, went their separate ways. Subsequently, the Argie ranks were divided and the Brits went on to claim the islands back for Margaret Thatcher and the watching millions back home.

Pete's other corker comes from a few inches up the map from Argentina in Brazil, home of amazing football, amazing women and the samba. But, according to Pete, the samba plays second fiddle to all-out rioting on match days in this sun-soaked soccer hotbed. No doubt when you think of Brazil you think of all the great players, fantastic matches and super goals to come out of the land of Pele's Beautiful Game. Edson Arantes do Nascimento, Jairzinho, Garrincha, Zico, Ronaldo and Gilberto Silva. Yeah, even John Barnes dancing around a load of gawping Brazilians to grab a wonder goal for England in the Maracana, the world's biggest football ground which once housed 200,000 screaming nutters going potty in support of their heroes. A footballing carnival, they call it. That's bollocks for starters. And we have Pete's word on that. Delve a little deeper, scratch around in the underbelly of Brazil and you'll find a thriving casual culture, with the HQ placed firmly in Rio. Copacabana Beach? You're having a laugh. You try laying out for a few rays on a sunbed on the golden sands when there is a big game on. No chance. You see the beach is where the majority of planned 'offs' take place. Top mobs can call on up to 400 boys with just a whistle from the beach. As the shrill reaches the sprawling flavelas, slums to you and me, there is a mad rush towards the shore as the rivals prepare to do battle. It is, Pete assures me, a sight to behold. And guess what? Seems the OB in Rio aren't as bad as our lot over here. NCIS's (National Criminal Intelligence Service) finest couldn't broker a deal like that in Brazil, which at least brings some order to fighting at football. They let the rival firms have access to the strip for the sole purpose of rucking and even have designated areas for it. I still laugh to this day remembering when Pete showed me pictures of signs telling tourists to stay off the beach during the specified times because all hell would be breaking loose. Now Pete's not saying the plod in Brazil are clueless. Far from it. They're a sneaky lot because back in 1985 they made a ground-breaking agreement with the self-proclaimed 'generals' of the clubs in Rio's main firms. On a sunny afternoon in a bar set back from the beach the top boys from Rio's four clubs, Fluminense, Flamengo, Botafogo and Vasco da Gama sat down to discuss the possibility of bringing the beach brawls in line with an officially sanctioned deal put together by the chief of police, Pele and assorted members of the clergy. Some four hours later, the historic pledge had been made and a deal that suited everyone had been struck. The 'generals' would be allowed to have their own time and space to get it on and, for their part, would ensure the defeated firms on any given day would carry out a litter patrol along the golden stretch of fine sand. Visit Rio today and you'll find that one of the worst insults you can hurl at a rival is "Go get your bin liner and clean up the beach." Hilarious really. By the way, Pete runs a bar in the Philippines with his Dad these days so if you're out that way and fancy a pint, call in to Para-Lytic in the main square in Manilla. And say hello from yours truly!

I reckon Pete is a lucky man in many respects. One of them is that he gets on really well with his old Dad. Now, I'm not saying I don't with mine, but I don't think we could ever have the same close relationship as those two. I often feel I'm just not on the same wavelength as my Pop. Not that I don't love the old geezer. But he is definitely a strange one. This was brought home to me recently when I thought I would have a go at tracing my family tree? You ever done it? You know the kind of thing: "Did I ever tell you my great second cousin twice removed was Noddy Holder from Slade?" and all that bollocks.

Well, I suppose we're all interested to know just how we come to be here as it is what makes us tick and all that. So, a few summers ago I thought I'd take a look at our family tree, go up to it and give it a bloody good shake. First point of call was aforementioned Dad Len. Now, with the old man, timing was everything. Speak to him before 6pm and there is no problem. But try to have a conversation after that and you are met with two major hurdles. The first is simple: where is he? Well for a start, don't waste time at home. If anyone calls up for my Dad after 6pm my dear old Mum assumes they're either mad or they've got the wrong number.

No, he won't be indoors but you don't really have to be Sherlock Holmes to find him, just do your homework.

**Monday**
The Crown with its big screen for SKY and Carlsberg at £1.20 a pint.
**Tuesday**
The Kings Head. Darts. Teachers at £1.50 for a double.
**Wednesday**
Conservative Club. Sherry £2.60 a schooner.
**Thursday**
Gay & Lesbian night at The Pink Pussycat. Guinness at £1.20.
**Friday**
Communist Club. 90% North Korean vodka £1.00 a belt.
**Saturday**
BNP meeting at The Royal Oak. John Bull Ale £1.20 a pint.
**Sunday**
Meet The Priest at St Matthews Catholic Church Hall. Holy wine is free. Drink as much as you like.

Yeah, you might have guessed, there's a theme running through my old man's week. The second problem is getting to him in time. Have a chat with him before 7pm and you'll never meet a more erudite, humorous, well-informed individual. Ater that forget it. You'll be wasting your time. One minute he'll be telling anyone in earshot that the Americans never went to the moon, next that Prince Charles doesn't really exist (all done with mirrors, apparently). Then, as the evening moves on, the topics of conversation can become more and more bizarre. "You know that Wayne Rooney? Back in 1973 me and him used to go birding every Saturday night down the Old Kent Road."

Anyway, I was able to sit down with the old man and have a chat about our lot. Just for a laugh, I brought a cassette recorder along and for the benefit of my family of the future here is the transcript of our "conversation". This interview was held on a Thursday night.

**Me**: So, Dad, you know I'm thinking of tracing our family tree. I'm interested to know about our ancestors. What do you remember about your father?

**Dad**: What? I can't hear you son. The fucking Scissor Sisters are too loud.

*I go to the bar to get the music turned down but it's still mad loud, almost unable to hear yourself think.*

**Me**: OK?

**Dad**: Who?

**Me**: What?

**Dad**: What?

**Me**: You.

**Dad**: Me?

**Me**: Yes.

**Dad**: What?

**Me**: Your father.

**Dad**: I know.

**Me**: What?

**Dad**: What?

**Me**: *(shouting)* Your father.

**Dad**: Yes.

**Me**: Well?

**Dad**: Fine, but getting thirsty.

**Me**: *(shouting)* Your father.

**Dad**: Who says I'm not? That fucking Mick Lee? That piece of shit. I'll swing for him. What's he been saying?

**Me**: Mick Lee?

**Dad**: Where is he? Has he put you up to this?

**Me**: Mick Lee? Is that the guy who helped you build our patio?

**Dad**: Sniffing round your Mum he was, what's he been saying?

**Me**: I don't want to hear any of this I want to know about your father, Gramps.

**Dad**: Gramps?

**Me**: Yeah, big United fan wasn't he?

**Dad**: Too right, went everywhere with them on his old motorcycle. Took him hours to get to places like Manchester and Liverpool. This was before motorways remember. Do me a favour, son, pop one in there for your old man.

*Tape turned off as I go to the bar.*

**Me**: Right, where were we, yeah...Gramps.

**Dad**: Who?

**Me**: Fuck me, Gramps!

**Dad**: Where?

**Me**: He was a big United fan, right?

**Dad**: Who?

**Me**: Gramps, Gramps was a big United fan.

**Dad**: I've just told you that, what's the matter with you?

**Me**: OK. Did he used to go with his mates?

**Dad**: Oh yeah. There was a gang of about seven or eight of them. A couple of them like Gramps had motorbikes, the others would get in the sidecars or they'd attach little wooden trolleys to the back and be dragged along. I remember as a nipper I was in one of the trolleys and went up to Newcastle. It took 16 hours.

**Me**: Was there any trouble at games back then?

**Dad**: Well, you have to remember this was in the late 1940s, just after the war, so most people had had a gut full of fighting and that. There was a lot of good feeling about, like the Summer of Love 1948 when teenagers started to wear flowers in their demob suits and start smoking powdered egg. A few of the lads who came back from the war formed a psychedelic commune next to the bombed gas works. Gramps had a little spell knocking about with them, you know he grew his hair, wore a kaftan and started on the old egg but it wasn't really him. Anyway, after a year or so it all seemed to fizzle out and they all joined the committee that organised the street party for the Coronation. Funny thing was, in 1967 when it all happened at Haight-Astbury, no one ever mentioned the 1948 scene.

**Me**: So how old was Gramps when he started going to games?

**Dad**: Let's see, he was born in 1921, did his bit in the war and...

**Me**: Did his bit in the war? That's a bit rich isn't it Dad?

**Dad**: Well he would have done his bit if he'd been allowed to.

**Me**: What, been allowed out of Wormwood Scrubs?

**Dad**: Listen you little bugger. Your grandfather could have been a great war hero, he had all the attributes of a great soldier. He was brave, fearless, looked great in a uniform.

**Me**:Yeah, he looked great in that one they gave him. The one with all the arrows on.

**Dad**: He could have made a great contribution to our armed forces if he had been given the opportunity.

**Me**: Well, yes. He could have contributed some of that lead he nicked off the roof of St Matthew's church, I suppose.

**Dad**: Stick one in there son, I'm gasping.

Tape turned off as I go to bar.

**Me**: OK, so....

**Dad**: What's this?

**Me**: What's what?

**Dad**: This...this ain't Guinness. It's a noncey, poncey girly cocktail. Bloody woman's drink, Jesus look at it with a bloody chunk of cucumber and a plastic umbrella in it. This ain't a proper drink, son.

**Me**: No, the Guinness is off. That's a "Long Snog With A Sweaty Miner". It's vodka, gin, rum and half of cider and it's only £1 tonight.

**Dad**: (Downs it in one). Mmm, not bad. Be a good lad, jump up and get us another one of these, what are they called again?"

**Me**: A "Long Snog With A Sweaty Miner"

I have to now explain, dear reader, that just at that moment, the final track on the Erasure retrospective CD ended, and my last sentence echoed around The Pink Pussycat Club causing many fellow drinkers to stare quizzically over to our table.

Tape turned off as I once again visit the bar.

**Me**: So, after Gramps did a bit of porridge for his adventures on the church roof, did he go into the army then?

**Dad**: No, he did 18 months and came out in 1942. He didn't fancy going off to war, not after the time he'd done in jail.

**Me**: So how did he avoid being cannon fodder?

**Dad**: Now promise me you'll never breathe a word of what I'm about to tell you, right?

**Me**: Of course, no problem.

**Dad**: Right (he beckons me nearer and looks conspiratorially around the bar). Ha, ha, ha, this is probably just the place to tell you. Remember that Quentin Crisp fella?

**Me**: Who?

**Dad**: The Naked Civil Servant and all that stuff. Used to ponce about London in high-heeled shoes, big hats, bras, corsets, with make-up and all that caper on.

**Me**: Oh, right, John Hurt.

**Dad**: When?

**Me**: What?

**Dad**: That to-do at Fulham Broadway after the Chelsea game wasn't it? Heard about it from Larry the Lamb when I was in The Three Crowns the other night.

**Me**: What are you on about?

**Dad**: When Fat John got hurt. A few Headhunters gave him a bit of a battering by all accounts.

**Me**: No! John Hurt, the bloody actor.

**Dad**: The Elephant Man and that jockey bloke who had cancer?

**Me**: Yeah, him.

**Dad**: Oh right, yeah. Anyway, you'll love this, you see your grandfather got out of the army by pretending to, you know...

**Me**: Pretending what?

**Dad**: Oh for God's sake son, use your brains, you know...

Once again, the final bars of a show tune tumbled from the speakers, just as I shouted...

**Me**: My Grandfather was a ponce?

Once again, our table became a source of interest to the bar regulars.

**Dad**: For Christ's sake son, keep your bloody voice down. God only knows what they think is going on over here. No, he was NOT a ponce, but he made out he WAS. The army didn't want benders and that in the barrack room and trenches, and nor did the other squaddies. So all he did was turn up to the army medical in all the gear with a voice Larry Grayson would have been proud of. Jesus, they couldn't get him out of that recruiting office quick enough!

**Me**: What did he do then?

**Dad**: Oh he had all the gear. He used to borrow dresses from his sister, old Bessie, pop a bit of slap on, a pair of sling-back shoes and totter about. He had to keep the charade up because there were police and Army all over the shop. If they sussed he was putting it on, his feet wouldn't have touched, son. He'd have either been back in clink or on the first boat off to the front.

**Me**: Did he go to any games in women's clothing?

**Dad**: Oh yeah, him and another five or six who were at it. Obviously, the normal league and cup programme was suspended during the war, but there were still loads of games on, and yeah, they'd tip up all wearing the gear.

**Me**: Jesus, what was the reaction when they arrived at the ground?

**Dad**: (Laughing) Oh sweet Jesus, it was like the Blitz and The Alamo all rolled into one! There was already a lot of bad feeling about these fellas like your Grandad not doing their duty for the war effort, but when they'd arrive at an away ground all dressed as women, well, the place would go mental!

**Me**: Where did they go dressed like that?

**Dad**: Well, United didn't exist as such during the war, all the players were fighting for King and Country, so Gramps and his crew would just pick a fixture each Saturday, turn up and take on the local lads and any uniformed blokes on leave who fancied a row. They didn't always get a result you know. Some nights he'd get home late in a terrible state, all the feathers ripped off his hat, bra straps cut, mascara and that all over the shop. But fair play to your Gramps and his crew, they more than normally stormed the home end and spent all afternoon taking liberties.

**Me**: Blimey, what a story.

**Dad**: Yeah, quite a lad your old Grandfather was, son. Quite a lad.

We thought that perhaps it was time to move on from The Pink Pussycat, as a number of the regulars had been eavesdropping on our conversation and I felt rather uneasy by all the attention. By now, the mix of drinks my father had consumed had made him somewhat unsteady on his feet. After popping my cassette machine back into my pocket, I had to slip an arm around the old codger and help him from the club, where once in the open air he demanded to be taken to the Bulls Head for a nightcap.

I lay in bed that night chuckling away, imagining my Grandfather and his mates, over 60 years ago, dressed in women's clothing fighting on the terraces. Quality.

# CHAPTER TEN

# Offs: the early years

Philip Larkin, some weirdo poet geezer whose stuff doesn't even rhyme, once said that

"Sexual intercourse began in 1963,
(which was rather late for me),
Between the end of the Chatterley ban and the Beatles' first LP".

Yeah, OK that rhymed, but most of his stuff seems to be about leaves and stuff. Same can be said about football hooliganism. Pick up any book written by any leftie so-called social historian and they'll tell you that before around 1969, all about our national game was sweetness and light. England were the World champions, opposing fans invited each other round for a spot of lunch before the match, we left our front doors open and little kids were passed over the heads of fans so they'd get a better view of the game.

Football was today's tai-chi, a touchy-feely, happy-clappy, after-you-Claude, let's-all-have-a-Buddhist chant thing.

Bollocks.

Yeah, well try explaining that to my cousin Ray who had six bells kicked out of him at Cold Blow Lane in 1968, or Uncle Stan who was given one hell of a slapping by a load of Everton lads who had come down to London to see The Beatles given their OBEs in 1965.

It makes things all very neat and tidy if we're told football hooliganism began on Wednesday 20th September 1969. But life ain't like that. Things don't work out like that. And that's why I opened

The National Museum of Football Hooliganism. Yeah, go on, have a laugh. Yeah, yeah – take the piss. But if you're really a top boy, a face in a decent mob, surely you'd be interested in just how you've got to be where you are now. It's an idea I've had for a few years. Jesus, they've got museums for teddy bears, torture, sex and paintings and that – why not one for firms?

You'd think a Labour government would be interested in backing a project that celebrated the culture of the working classes wouldn't you? I mean, I'm sorry I'm not gay, black, in a wheelchair or from an oppressed eastern European regime – I'm just a white working class bloke who, along with thousands of others every week, goes to watch football and if given half a chance will have it with a mob from the opposing club. That's what I do. That's me.

I'm thinking, lottery grants. I'm thinking all that dough splashing about in the cultural wine lake. These characters put the dough up for dodgy leftie theatre groups to piss around with plays about single mothers or for a bunch of unwashed grunge merchants to spray their graffiti on the walls of sheltered housing and call it urban art.

So, I gave them a call. I got through to the bird who dealt with all the grant applications – first question: "Are you gay, disabled or from some tin-pot, one-eyed tip somewhere in the Balkans? If you are, there's a cheque here with your name on." "No, I'm white, male and working class, and I need about 10 big ones to start up the National Museum of Football Hooliganism." Click, burrrrrr.

Get the picture?

So, the nonces in the government weren't going to give me any assistance. Why didn't that surprise me? When have any governments ever cared about working class culture?

Oh, if it kicks off big style in Iraq or Northern Ireland, or The Somme or Flanders – oh yeah, then they'll come calling for us but not now. Not in peace time.

So what was I to do? I did what that old geezer Norman Tebbitt recommended a few years back, I got on my bike and decided to set the museum up myself.

After a couple of weeks hunting about, I found the premises I was looking for.

A shop on the high street, once a newsagents. The place had closed down more than five years before, and by the looks of it, not a soul had entered the place since the last copy of The Sun had been sold. It was a lot bigger than it looked from the outside and I reckoned with a bit of spit and polish could be a little goldmine.

First things first, I had to sew the lease up, put a few readies down for rent and that, and suddenly bingo – I was the proud proprietor of the world's first museum for football hooliganism.

The first couple of weeks were hard graft, basically gutting the place – the skip man and I became very close friends. Dad came down to have a look and was his normal supportive self. "What a fucking tip, you must be off your bloody trolley, even if you manage to do this place up, who the fuck wants to see a museum dedicated to a load of mindless nutters?". Yeah, Yeah, we'll see. Build it, and they will fucking come, mate – they will fucking come, I thought.

Slowly, I began to get things ship shape. Like most firms, ours contained a good variety of tradesmen, so it wasn't difficult to put a bit of pressure on a few plasterers, call in a couple of favours from a brickie or two, and remind a chippie that if it wasn't for me up at Roker Park ten years ago, he would have been resting in the Royal Wearmouth Infirmary for at least a couple of weeks. As happens when a new venture starts to appear, I had the usual questions about what the shop was going to be, when was I going to open – you know, all the stuff the local busybodies wanted to chat about over tea and biscuits.

"Ooh, a museum, wonderful – just what this town needs. Tell me, what kind of museum?" Then, when they found out, it was, whoosh – they were gone.

After a few more weeks, the place looked the dogs. The museum was ready – all I needed now were the exhibits. The first batch of stuff was easy to get hold of – it was gear that me and my firm had picked up over the years. A chair leg that had put Leicester's top boy on his arse, an OB helmet that had been liberated from its owner at a skirmish on Marylebone station's Platform 2, the original manuscript of our firm's song, which had been composed by a couple of our top boys on a five-hour train journey up to Anfield in the late 80s. But this was all very well, what I really needed was some tip-top stuff that lads from all over the country, and even worldwide would beat a path to my door to have gander at.

Have you ever been to Christies or Sotheby's? Me neither. Think ponces and nonces and you won't be far wrong.

I got on the blower and asked for Christies' head honcho who dealt with all the football gear. Sure enough I got through to some chinless wonder whose name was Quentin double-barrel. "Well yes, our next football memorabilia auction is in three week, what kind of exhibits are you looking for?" he said. "Have you got any of the seats the Millwall lads tore up and chucked at the OB when they rioted at Luton?"

"Is this some kind of a joke?" he asked.

"I'll tell you the joke, my old china, you...you big, tarty, fucking, wanking queen." Looked like I was going to go elsewhere for my exhibits. Although of course these mugs have changed their tune now they can see that serious collectors of this stuff are prepared to part with big money to get their hands on this gear.

You ever been on eBay? Course you have. What a bloody idea that is. So simple. People emptying their lofts of all the old rubbish and selling it to some bloke living in California.

Online I went onto eBay to see what was on offer.

So, football hooliganism only started a few decades back did it? I didn't think so.

What do you need for a good off? I'll tell you. Booze, a load of blokes and a football game, right? Well, all those ingredients were there back in the mid 1800s, so surely hooliganism must have been rife. Thing is, back then there was no real media to report it. There were newspapers and books and that, but it looks to me that they were all written by blokes like Dickens, and I don't mean Alan.

There were all sorts on there. A veritable Aladdin's Cave in cyber consisting of everything from a First World War mustard gas container which had been thrown at the referee during a Millwall v Chelsea London reserve league game in 1919, to a pair of hob-nailed boots worn by Liverpudlian docker Fred Quinn. Not know of Quinn? Neither did I until I did a bit of digging. It didn't tale long to unearth this character who would easily get a place as a top boy with our lot even today. Quinn was widely accepted as being the hardest man in Merseyside back at the turn of the century and was Tranmere daft. The boots were, claimed the seller, the very same pair that were worn when Quinn volleyed Rochdale's main man Godfrey Horne in the head "causing him to die". Quinn was tried, found guilty of unlawful killing and hanged. The boots were said to have been sold to the hangman for a shilling on the morning of the public execution outside the Liver Building, which Quinn, along with all his other worldly possessions, had bequeathed to Tranmere Rovers, his first and, tragically, last love. I was outbid for the "daisy roots" by former Prenton Park manager John Aldridge. Aldridge has the largest Rovers memorabilia collection in the world so they are in a good home and John has since been in touch to say he will loan the museum the boots for an upcoming exhibition we have planned entitled "Kick to kill – football's deadliest footwear". Nice one, Aldo.

Another item I missed out on still leaves me sick to my stomach even now. It would have been close to taking pride of place in the museum, if only I'd have been on my game. Somehow I failed to realise just how serious a rival bidder was when an extremely rare item surfaced about a year after we had opened the museum doors to the public. Admittedly, I'd been on the source down at The Lion one Sunday afternoon and when I got back I just couldn't resist getting the laptop out and getting on eBay. I wasn't particularly expecting to find anything great for the museum but I also collect American sneakers from the 1950s and was hopeful of securing a pair of original yellow Converse which were still in the box and were unworn. But I digress. So there I am skipping from section to section, meandering around that great superhighway market stall, when one advert in particular caught my attention. It read:

ORIGINAL 1920s SPORTING TROPHY

This sterling silver cup was the prize for the first and last Association Football challenge match between the London constabulary and a hooligan element who attached themselves to soccer clubs for the sole purpose of "disruption, fisticuffs and rioting".

Basically, this was very much an unofficial game between the OB and the main faces in the London firms of the 20s. It was perfect for us. The starting bid was £499 but I knew that wouldn't last when some of the main players got wind. It was probably worth at least that melted down. Somewhere in the dim and distant past I remember seeing a reference to the match, a newspaper cutting or even the match programme, and it was how the encounter was billed which struck me: "Rozzers v Ruffians".

Again, the internet came to my rescue as there was no way I could find the reference material I would need to check it out in my loft. Most modern search engines have fantastic capacity and I suppose I could have tried Google of even Ask Jeeves. But, when something as rare as this little beauty surfaces, there is only one place to go for the seasoned hooligan artefact collector: www.hooligle.com. You have to be a member, of course, but there ain't too much out there this site will miss. Sure enough, a few seconds after typing in the relevant keywords up came just what I was looking for.

It was a report from the now defunct London Evening Chronicle by an A.H. Hill, who, because of how sensitive the plod chiefs would have been to their officers in effect consorting with knows hoodlums, wasn't aware of exactly how the teams were made up.

Urchins overrun opponents to land inaugural cup

"A cold, blustery and altogether unseasonably cold May afternoon at Hackney Marshes witnessed the first match between 'Constabulary' and 'Urchins', with the latter being triumphant and securing the London Challenge Cup by an emphatic score line of six goals to two."

It went on in a similar manner with our Mr Hill recounting a blow-by-blow match report using surnames from the provided team-sheet. Of course, these were all aliases. The real story wasn't told that day but can be found in a diary kept by one of the "ruffians", a bloke by the name of Bernard Simpson, known as Razors for his weapon of choice. To spare you the trawl through the diary, which, again I found through Hooligle, it boiled down like this: One Saturday night in 1926 after a particularly lively West Ham v Tottenham match at Upton Park, the OB of the day challenged Tottenham's firm to a match to "settle some scores". Apparently some cozzers had been caught unawares and had to run for their lives to escape a beating. The Spurs lads took it a step further and agreed to the game if they could make it a Ruffians XI drawn up from mobs in the capital. Razors was in charge and he selected the following team with, as he says in his diary, "what was without any degree of prejudice given my own devotion to the Lillywhites of White Hart Lane".

Chopper Maguire (*Spurs*)
Razors Simpson (*Spurs*) Nutter Brunton (*Clapton Orient*)
Syrup Smith (*West Ham*)
Punchy Watkins (*Brentford*) Samuel Brown (*The Arsenal*)
Harmer Wells (*Chelsea*) Rory O'Moore (*The Arsenal*)
Joe Pyes (*Crystal Palace*)
Dicky Harnett (*Charlton Athletic*) Pip Turner (*Fulham*)

So the Ruffians took the honours and the cup was awarded but there was no real glory for the hoolies that day. All but Razors and Turner were nicked later that night at a disturbance in the Cheddar Cheese in Fleet Street while celebrating their victory. They'd chosen the boozer because there was a late night engravers open and they clubbed together the three shillings it cost to have the following inscription on it: Ruffians XI, Winners, London Challenge Cup, 1927. The cup was lost in the raucous celebrations which led to fighting and trouble which led to the arrests but the trophy was found by a paper boy in an alley the next morning. He handed it in at the nearby offices of the Daily Sketch where a football correspondent name of Lanky Danson got his hands on it. In his possession it stayed until Lanson bit the dust and his attic was cleared by realtives. It was one of them who had shoved it on eBay.

I knew I would have to dig deep into the museum's little nest egg to land this prised exhibit and reckoned on spending up to a grand to do so. But, as I mentioned, I'd had a few beers and, well, I'd failed to see the "Buy Now" option on the advert for £500. Obviously another keen-eyed collector had noticed it and bought the bleeding thing from right under my nose. I was gutted and to this day think the cup would probably have taken centre stage. Oh well.

I did have, and have had, some successes online though

On another of my trawls through eBay, I found a geezer in Texas selling "Ye Olde Book Of Association Football Shenanigans, Disturbances and Misunderstandings – 1883". Now this character obviously had no idea just what he had on his hands. He had a couple of bids for the book, but I played it cagey and nipped in at the last minute to snap it up for the princely sum of £5 – and make no mistake, that's the best "skin diver" I've ever spent.

When the book arrived, it was everything I'd hope for and more. There were blow-by-blow accounts of firms at each other as far back as 1874, and a marvellous account of a great off at Kennington Oval before the Royal Engineers and Old Etonians played out the FA Cup final of 1875.

The book was written by a fella by the name of Samuel Glossop, who called himself "The Sporting Buccaneer". Old Samuel followed The Royal Engineers, who by all accounts had perhaps the nastiest little following of the Victorian age.

Here's Samuel's account of what they got up to at an away game at Blackburn Rovers in 1890.

"And lo, verily, the day at last came whence we the followers and loyal defenders of the faith of Royal Engineers would travel north-north-west to Blackburn Rovers football club for a FA Cup challenge match of the highest calibre. The men of the northern Rovers team had just, in the previous months moved to their new arena or stadium located at Ewood Park. Personally, I had a fondness for the Rovers previous position on Leamington Road, so I travelled with a heavy heart. However my mood improved some as at the railway terminus of Kings Cross St Pancras I fell into social intercourse with my fellow Royal Engineers followers, many of whom were indeed engineers of some standing and stood still clothed in their working overalls and caps, and many carrying signs of their mechanical labour including many daubings of oils and petroleum spirits on their skin and clothing. This made the air immediate to them somewhat acrid and unpleasant to those not used to the toil of a mechanical demeanour. I, myself, had to resort to a liberal inhalation of lavender water purchased from a grubby boy at the station's platform. He initially demanded a half penny for the bottle, but I told the guttersnipe in no uncertain terms, that to ask such an outrageous financial tariff for such a paltry amount of his perfumed concoction was tantamount to having a giraffe at my expense. His mood became somewhat dark as he continued to argue his case, although he became agitated but then acceptant of my offer of one farthing for the lavender water as he seemed to understand that my position amongst the followers of the Royal Engineers could cause him to be on the wrong end of a severe thrashing.

I could hardly contain myself as only a few moments later, I saw another travelling spectator press a three penny bit into the oik's hand for a bottle, the exact same as the one I had just purchased. The cheeky rogue gave me a sly wink before moving off down the station to find another poor fellow with more money than sense.

Soon, the steam locomotive arrived at the platform, welcomed with a hearty cheer and a throaty rendition of "We Are All Engineers". The noise was most impressive, and fair nearly lifted the roof right off the station and toward the heavens above.

Once aboard the locomotive, I felt we numbered around

three hundred souls, a most acceptable total of followers. Many were what we called "Rosette Boys" – young men whose interest in the day was the game, and the game only. These fresh faced, earnest young men would, during the journey, read the scriptures or create paintings with water colours or pencils. I, as was the usual custom sat at the rear of the carriage amongst the more zealous supporters of the Royal Engineers. We numbered around twenty, and would announce our status to all and sundry on a regular basis with a repertoire of colourful, imaginative and occasionally bawdy sonnets and verses, some of which would make a grown man blush such was their vulgarity. We did indeed tend to stand apart from our fellow supporters. Our garb was somewhat more decorative, our watch chains and spats all of a similar design, our top hats from the very best milliners and our whiskers were oiled and shaped into some most satisfying shapes. Amongst our brotherhood, for that is indeed what it had become, the wearing of beautiful waistcoats made of the finest silk imported from China were de rigeur. These astonishing pieces of clothing cost the best part of a working man's monthly wage, and how many of our band afforded such ostentatious items of apparel was a common mystery to many who crossed our path.

As the train journey proceeded so too did the imbibing of strong liquor, tobacco and snuff. Indeed, by the time our locomotive pulled into the terminus of Crewe to take on water and coal, many of our party had clearly over done the refreshments and were clearly suffering from sickness and vomiting. It was during this brief stay at Crewe where we fell amongst some local ruffians and a number of scuffles took place. One particularly revolting individual took it on himself to board our carriage and urinate on a sleeping Rosette Boy. This foul act provoked my associates and I to such a level that we threw ourselves upon this lout and boxed his ears to such an extent that the man begged to be thrown back onto the platform This we did with relish once our locomotive had raised its speed to a breathtaking five miles an hour. The poor fellow collided with the asphalt before continuing his journey into an array of packages and wooden crates awaiting transportation south to the capital.

The sight of this bounder reaping what he had sown raised the spirits of the whole carriage, and even the poor bedraggled Rosette Boy who had been the recipient of the invaders' foul liquid seemed to put the incident behind him and join us in lusty song.

Our journey continued through the counties of Cheshire and Lancashire, the sight of the mills and chimneys causing much amusement amongst those of our number of whom had not before ventured to these parts of the Empire. The fashion for the wearing of heavy wooden clogs had not, and in my heart would never, been taken up by us metropolitan types, and the first viewing of locals regaled in such outlandish footwear caused much mirth and not a little pity amongst the travelling support.

Soon, it was clear to all aboard the locomotive that we were approaching the town of Blackburn, and within minutes our train, having long since left the capital, arrived in a cloud of steam and not a little blowing of the driver's whistle at our destination.

With great haste, we vacated the carriage, all of us impatient and excited to at last tread on northern land. There to meet us were members of the Blackburn constabulary. Large round faced men who seemed not to possess a jot of humour or education between them. They spoke in a harsh indistinct manner making them nigh on impossible to understand.

As well as their dark blue uniforms and helmets, they held gnarled wooden truncheons and made it plain that if we were even contemplating any behaviour that they deemed to be unsuitable or frivolous, it would be their pleasure to break our heads with said tools of violence. This show of force was indeed successful, and we agreed that if we were to act in a somewhat ridiculous manner that afternoon, it was not to be at the railway terminus or under the eye of these burly policemen.

However, as we left the terminus a shrill shout came from the street outside and I lie not when I say we were immediately set upon by a highly excited mob, all of whom wore the blue and white favours of Blackburn Rovers. They rained down blows on as many of our party as they could, using the coarsest and most vulgar language I had the misfortune of hearing before or since. I looked in horror as the Rosette Boys bore the brunt of this assault, the poor fellow who had been urinated on at Crewe must have walked under a number of ladders and trodden on many gaps in the pavement that day, as he now was on the receiving end of more than a baker's dozenof hardy kicks from be-clogged and hobnailed booted feet.

The Peelers, who had summarily warned our contingent of the hazards of being involved in such an exhibition of social unrest simply stood back from the proceedings, giving their local brethren free rein to indulge in this sport. I was able to see the faces of the uniformed men, and it was clear they were enjoying the spectacle of we travellers from the capital receiving such abuse. However, it was clear to myself and my more seasoned sporting followers, that perhaps this unruly mob had assumed we were all prepared to blindly accept such treatment, and it was noticeable that those who sported the colours of the home club became somewhat lackadaisical and downright foolhardy in their actions, some lighting their clay pipes whilst they assaulted our Rosette Boys, others acting in an even more folly-ish style by holding conversations with passers-by and discussing plans for a charabanc ride out to Morecambe Bay during the forthcoming Wakes Week.

Their over-confidence was breathtaking, their sheer audacity drawing gasps of astonishment from myself and my colleagues. It was then I decided we had experienced quite enough of this behaviour, and in a clear forthright manner I encouraged those who had travelled north by means of the locomotive to "Stand". Immediately, the tone of the proceedings were altered, and with just a very few hand signals and a tweak of my moustache I was able to muster the complete party of Royal Engineers supporters into a compact and organised platoon. This sudden change of demeanour caused consternation and confusion amongst the home ranks, who until now had enjoyed some five minutes akin to catching fish in a barrel. One of our number, sensing a possible change in fortunes, one William Bradley, a joiner by trade from Tooting Bec and a well known amateur pugilist, took it upon himself to seek personal retribution upon a number of who seemed to be the ring leaders of our welcome committee. He indeed was successful in his task, setting a number to flight with just a few well-timed blows. Mr Bradley's deeds gave us good heart, and from then on with the steam, we went in, returning blows we had received many times over. It was with great joy we witnessed the once seemingly invincible band of Rovers followers rush away from the terminus in every direction as a gaggle of ill disciplined sheep or some such other livestock would. It was then I instructed my fellow supporters to join me in a rousing rendition of "We Are All Engineers" – never before had that melody sounded so sweet to the human ear.

As men, we all now felt somewhat like giants, and we marched with purpose to Ewood Park and the match. It was noticeable, the members of the local constabulary, who not a thrice before were merrily enjoying our plight, had clearly considered their position and accepted that perhaps the visitors who had alighted from the steaming loco were tidy, and not to be trifled with.

With that in mind, we were given a generous and amiable escort to the newly constructed grandstand at Ewood Park. Many locals had come out from their austere dwellings to line the cobbled streets, those of a more aggressive disposition shouted oaths and threats towards our party, many, including woman and babes made threatening gestures with their hands.

On arrival at the ground where the match was to be played,

each and every one of us were charged the princely sum of two pence to be allowed entry via a wrought iron turnstile. The more nimble minded amongst our following were able to calculate that this day, Blackburn Rovers were to make a tidy sum in revenue from the great support the Royal Engineers brought to this challenge match. A mighty roar came up from the home following as they enjoyed our entrance to the section of the grandstand where we would enjoy this sporting spectacle, and some of the more waggish among them sang a variety of music hall songs, all making humorous remarks at our expense. Many of us who had travelled from London were now in need of some kind of refreshment, and we were all delighted to find a wooden kiosk where four busty northern maids sold a variety of hot pies and other savoury dishes. The women worked quickly and with good grace to ensure we all received our orders before the game began.

It was then the two teams took to the field, Blackburn Rovers decked out in a fine display of blue and white shirts, knicker-bockers and stockings, our favourites proudly ran on to our applause in a mustard and red outfit. The scene was most colourful and pleasing to the eye. The referee, a Mr Pollard from Barnsley blew his whistle and the captains from teams met in the centre circle to shake hands and exchange pennants.

Once the pre-match formalities had taken place, the football stadium, by now fairly bursting at the seams with sports followers, seemed to erupt with a ferocious outburst of shouts and songs. The Blackburn centre forward, a tall man with a handle bar moustache kicked the ball towards the Royal Engineers goal with great gusto and the match began. The leather ball was kicked to and fro by each team, with little or no reason or rhyme. The first half of the tie continued in this manner, with neither team able to deposit the ball in the opposition goal. During the interval in play, I noticed a number of local ruffians move from their section towards where we Royal Engineers followers were spectating this exciting cup match. As the second half commenced, their numbers grew, and they began to gesture at us in a most ungentlemanly manner. Suddenly, on our inside right, a young man by the name of Hall, dispossessed the home full back and shot the ball into the Rovers goal net. Pandemonium around the stadium ensued, this goal brought we Engineers men much satisfaction, however the Blackburn supporters did not share our enthusiasm for the match and their mood grew blacker. They had now almost completely surrounded our part of the grandstand and their songs were now laced with poisonous threats and prophecies. One of their band shouted to me if I and my colleagues wanted some, I replied in the affirmative, and added for good measure that I was quite prepared to box his ears until the cows came home.

The Peelers, by now aware that some kind of nuisance was to take place made their best efforts to quell the ardour of the Rovers mob, but their attempts were in vain as the home support easily broke through their lines and set upon us. This time, the Rosette Boys moved aside, aware that we, the more experienced followers would take care of any disturbance. The home supporters finding their passage into our area unprotected grew in stature, and began again to fill the air with their songs and chants. The constabulary, now hopelessly outnumbered and seemingly aware that they too could be injured in any potential skirmish, lost heart, some of them finding shelter behind the now closed savoury pie kiosk. I instructed my fellows to allow the Blackburn bounders into our section, then with a shrill cry I ordered all Engineers men to "Steam in gentlemen, steam in!"

We set upon those poor fellows with great gusto, and I do believe they believed they had descended in Hell itself, and we, the Engineers were Satan, Lucifer, Old Nick and his vile helpers all combined into one. We fought these invaders with great spirit, and within no time they had wished they had lazed in front of their fire hearth that very day. The grandstand was soon littered with their top hats and other pieces of finery, as they turned tail and fled from whence they came. We were triumphant, however the situation was about to improve tenfold as Mills, our towering centre-half sent a powerful header into the roof of the Rovers net. The game was ours, both on the field and in the grandstand. These twin assaults on the northerners' pride deflated them so, and within moments the once cocky and arrogant home supporters were an army in retreat as they streamed from the Ewood grandstands, back onto the cobbled streets and into their alehouses to perhaps drown their sorrows and lick their wounds.

We, the Royal Engineers, as both players and supporters celebrated a great victory with many hurrahs and songs such as "For They Are Jolly Good Fellows" and it was with a fine voice and a full heart that we marched victoriously back to the railway terminus to alight the locomotive back south to London and our loved ones. The carriage was indeed a merry place to behold with much guffawing and more songs. Each of our number would in turn inform his peers of his fine performance in the grandstand that afternoon, and it was noticeable as the ale flowed, the stories of these daring deeds became more and more akin to a fairy story. Yet none of our number would correct another as we all basked in such glory and victory. We would all await the London Times the following Monday, whence the Thunderer would inform us all of the draw for the following round of the F.A. Challenge Cup, and whom we would have to defeat to continue our quest for this fine trophy."

See? Nearly 150 years ago, lads were travelling up and down the country to have it with another firm. And notice the OB? Yeah, some things never change, eh?

This Samuel Glossop geezer was perhaps the world's first top boy. Quality stuff.

The book really is an eye opener, there's a list of what the main faces wore, who the top firms were, a real in-depth look at how hooliganism started. I can't recommend it enough. If you ever see a copy -snap it up, you won't be sorry.

To really get the museum going I started to travel up and down the country attending hooligan car boot sales. These are a fairly recent innovation, the first and still the biggest and best is the one held in the car park at Elland Road every Sunday morning. One tip if you do fancy Hoolie-Booting, is get there early. Often, by 9.30am all the really good gear is gone. I admit, it's much more difficult to get hold of any really incredible stuff – hoolie memorabilia prices have gone through the roof, and as I mentioned earlier the big London auction houses are now getting involved, hosting big hoolie auctions three or four times a year. What really did put hoolie memorabilia on the map was the special programme that David Dickinson did on BBC1 over Christmas. Dickinson used to run with the Kippax lads at City in the late 1960s, so you have to listen to this fella when he starts to talk. He knows his stuff. But now, with all this media interest, prices are going way beyond the normal punter. For instance, at the end of last year I picked up a piece of the Wembley crossbar the Jocks broke up in 1977. I paid £60 which included a certificate of authenticity signed by Barmy Mick from Edinburgh, now sadly no longer with us – and I thought that was a bit toppy. There was a guy from Dundee with a smaller piece getting bids of over £300 on eBay last week – crazy money.

But all this interest and mad money makes my museum a real goer. These lads can't afford the stuff they want, so they'll have to shell out a tenner to come to my museum, and then spend a few more quid in my gift shop. I'm on a winner. And don't forget, when you do tip up at my museum, do say hello.

# CHAPTER ELEVEN

# Wheelchair wonders and the yellow peril

DISABLED dazzlers. Wheelchair wonders. Call 'em what you like...or not as any right-minded politically correct bod will tell you. Crap. Not so long ago there were disabled firms roaming our grounds causing havoc, mayhem and making a nuisance of themselves and they didn't give a flying fuck about names, I can tell you. Remember sticks and stones? Exactly. They break bones, but names, well they'll never hurt you. Any of you. These top disabled boys revelled in their wheeled-up wrong-doing and went by names that would have any Guardian reader reaching for the quill to fire off a worthy letter to the organ demanding an investigation. Crap again. Meet West Brom's tidy Throstle Crips...a name later 'borrowed' by our gun-totin' cousins across the pond in Los Angeles (the Crips bit, not the Throstles part, although there is to this day healthy interest in the Baggies in certain no-go areas of crime-ridden Compton). Welcome Berslam Gimp Alert, who are Port Vale's very own handicapped heavies. Try Sheffield United's Bedridden Blades for size. The SUBBs were at a distinct disadvantage when it came to the fine art of football hooliganism. The very nature of their conditions meant they were never able to get out of bed and so the only way they could vent their anger and support of the Bramall Lane outfit was to hurl abuse at other mobs via emails and mobile phones. If Sheffield United main firm, the BBC, had a particularly busy workload of a weekend, members of the SUBBs would step in and carry out various administrative tasks to help the violence go smoothly. Very often rival firms would be chatting to a SUBB on the mobile to arrange a scrap thinking all along they were on to main geezer. Fair play to the SUBBs, game as fuck in their own way.

And they were not alone.

Everton have always managed to raise a good firm and they could also call upon a decent disabled mob, too. The Gladys Street Cutters were a horrible bunch of Mickey Mousers, who were tooled up and willing to slash any foe at the drop of a forged disabled parking permit. The Cutters were ruthless and took no prisoners. Everyone was fair game in their eyes and I think a lot of the leading boys were bitter and twisted about being in their unfortunate position. Their devotion to the cause was unswerving and they were more of a cult than a gang. They even had one gang member, Lenny the Lemon, who had disabled himself on purpose just so he could be part of their mob. This lot were hardcore. At the helm was a strange looking character who went by the name of Aubrey Lewis Booth, known to one and all across Merseyside as Big Boothy. He was a giant of a man with an abundance of facial hair and who never went anywhere without his trusty pet Jack Russell dog called Rasta. Big Boothy had lost both his legs during a terrible accident while unloading cargo down at Albert Docks. Turns out a container packed with bananas in from Jamaica came down on him on a frosty Monday morning totally crushing his legs and forcing doctors to operate and take the limbs off just above both knees. The average time it takes patients to get over this sort of operation is a year, possibly two. Big Boothy was not having that. He had the legs amputated, had got his Mum to find a top-notch wheelchair and she wheeled him out of the hospital and along to Goodison on the Wednesday night after the accident in time for Everton's crucial FA Cup replay against local rivals Liverpool. They lost 3-0. Rasta was nicked at half-time for peeing on a copper.

Boothy worshipped one-time Everton midfielder Kevin Richardson to the point where he wore a permanent cast on his arm in tribute to the player's appearance with one in some important game or another. The majority of the Cutters lived as one in a big Victorian house on the fringes of Stanley Park and it was from here, under the guidance of Big Boothy, they planned attack after attack, week after week back in the late 70s when they were responsible for some of the nastiest acts of hooliganism ever witnessed. One weekend late in the season in 1978 they lost the plot totally and caused carnage with an attack on a group of boy scouts who were attending a jumble on a match day in a nearby school. The Cutters had been up all night planning for the visit of hated rivals Manchester United and had taken a cocktail of pills, booze and Colombian hurry-up dust so they could work deep into the night. But with all highs come the lows and this mixture eventually brought on paranoia and that was when it happened. Dregs Tony, Spats Chris and a few others had been on a recognisance mission just after lunch and had mistakenly taken the scouts as Mancs trying to hoodwink them by sneaking in under the guise of being Baden Powell's finest. In no time they had reported back to Big Boothy, raised the rest of their crew and were on the warpath. They steamed into the startled scouts and the sound of Stanley knife opening up young flesh was everywhere. It was horrible and there were many casualties. The frightening fight made some national newspapers but the biggest outcry came from the Liverpool Daily Examiner which ran a front page story headlined: Shame of the knife yobs. One of the more colourful national tabloids ran the same story under the banner: Scousers scalp scouts. Jimmy Young even had one of the scout leaders on his Radio Two show. This was big news.

But one little known fact never reported was just how game some of the scouts were. They were a pack visiting Liverpool from Warrington and had some good lads on board. At one point they had turned at least half a dozen Everton lads out of their wheelchairs and were shoeing those who hadn't crawled to safety but the numbers did for them and they retreated to their mini-bus with a trip to hospital for a date with some cotton and thread.

The Cutters never really recovered form the bad press they received after the Stanley Park scout rumble and a gap that already existed between them and Everton's able-bodied scally firm grew to such an extent that there was regular clashes between the two. The final firecracker in the breadbin came when Big Boothy met an American housewife over the internet and eventually moved to Boston to be with his new woman. The clan drifted apart. The huge house in which they had lived so happily for so long was sold off and is now a halfway house for glue-sniffers. Rasta went to live with Big Boothy's mum and another chapter in the story of disabled football hooligans came to its natural conclusion.

Everton were a good, hard firm but blew it big time, which just kept them away from top spot in my book.

That particular honour goes to a fearsome gang of hoolies that would give any firm a run for their money, the infamous Spurs Casual Spastics. I know, the name is not particularly PC, but that was the point. If you don't get it, you're not meant to.

The SCS ruled the roost for years and no-one could touch 'em when it came to a bit of bovver. They were a nasty firm who could call on big numbers for big matches. I remember one north London derby I attended with TV soccer pundit Chloe Tomlinson, who at the time worked for Arsenal as a Press Officer. She may have worked over at Gooner Mansions but our Chloe is a big Spurs fan. I met her through our mutual mate Bryan Robson (more of which later) and she invited me to the Lane with colleague Mark Bucklan for the visit of their friendly rivals down the Seven Sisters Road, Arsenal. The Gooners had a reasonable disabled turn-out who went by the name of the GIs (it stands for Gooners Incapacitated) and while they couldn't call on more than about 20 boys, those they did have wouldn't wheel away from anyone and had gained a lot of respect for doing so. They were disably led by a character known as Monktash Adrian after it turned out he had a sideline acting in disabled gay porn films. He was a woofter but tough with it. There was always fun and games when they pitched up and this time round was no exception. Chloe and Mark had gone into the ground for a pie so I agreed to meet them later and sneaked off to a boozer called the British Queen, not far from White Hart Lane overground rail station. I got a few stares but felt comfortable as I was wearing a

Chas and Dave T-shirt. I bought a pint of lager, found the jukebox and livened up the place a bit with some Duran Duran. Big mistake. Unbeknown to me, one of the Eighties band's roadies was a big Gooner who had persuaded Simon LeBon to included a clip of Arsenal winning the league at the Lane in 1971 in the video for their hit song Rio. Look carefully next time and in one scene you can see hundreds of red and white-clad Gunners fans invading the pitch after the dramatic victory at the home of their deadliest rivals. "What did you put that on for?" The voice sounded familiar but I carried on perusing the tracks on offer on the jukebox, Stand and Deliver by Adam Ant was to be my next choice. The almost robotic voice repeated: "I said, 'What did you put that on for?'" Where had I heard that voice before? Fuck it, I thought. I need to front this up sooner rather than later. Others in the pub had started to take an interest in me. The usual pre-match chatter had virtually stopped and all you could hear was the sound of a syphon as one drinker added a splash of tonic to his gin. By now there was total silence. As they say in the old war films my Dad used to watch dressed in his combats: "It's quiet...too quiet."

I made sure my Chas and Dave top could be clearly seen as I turned round...to be confronted by none other than a Stephen Hawking lookalike. Not only did the crumpled up geezer look like famous theoretical physicist, he sounded like him as well. I had to play it right or I would have got a pasting on my first visit to Tottenham without our mob. That's a massive loss of face in my book. As usual, I knew the score, knew how to handle this tricky situation. Why, I'd been in the same plot countless times. Except not with spastics. I patted the powerless paraplegic on the head, took a swig of Kronie, smiled and said: "Good band, mate. Not as good as these two chirpy Cockneys, though," pointing to Chas and his cheeky smile and Dave with his beard on my T-shirt. Laughter broke out and the tension was gone in an instant. I was relieved. I had maintained face and given the boys a laugh. They were now my pals. For the time being.

The lads then explained their dislike of Duran Duran because of the video and told me "Hawking" was in fact Chariot (a combination of Charlie Marriot, his actual name), one of Tottenham's top disabled boys. A good ten minutes later, I kid you not, Chariot had tapped in the entire lyrics to the Chas and Dave hit Ossie's Dream into his little voice box machine and was now merrily singing them out in honour of my T-shirt and some little Argentinian who couldn't speak English very well. Remember Ossie Ardiles? Fair play. More of the Argies later.

The story behind Chariots is a sad one and one which me of all people should take notice of and probably learn from. Yeah, right. Fuck that. Fair play, though, Charlie had been a main player in the able-bodied Spurs ranks before his accident but, Jesus, he knew what he was doing. We all do. Well, some of us don't. One evening after Tottenham had played a pre-season friendly up in Glasgow against Partick Thistle, Charlie and his boys decided to take advantage of a late-night opening at the nearby Museum of Transport. But, as is the norm in the majority of these tales of woe, drink had been take to a large extent. The story goes that Charlie refused to back down before the game in the Jags Social Club when he was challenged to a whisky drinking competition with Thistle's legendary fan and former bodyguard to the Ian Dury (of Blockheads fame) Amir Khan. This bloke could drink for Scotland but Charlie matched him shot for shot and the contest was declared a draw because kick-off was minutes away. But the wee drams had taken their toll and Charlie slept through the game and missed, as the Maryhill Shopper newspaper recorded, an "entertaining 0-0 draw". More beers were supped after the game and the boys decided to take in the museum after a bus ride through to the Kelvin Hall area. By the time the 20-strong Tottenham mob had paid their £1.50 entrance to the museum, Charlie was out of his bonce. And that's when the terrible accident happened which would condemn this 27-year-old flower arranger from St Albans to a motionless and speechless life. While the other boozed casuals took in the impressive collection of pre-war motorcyles, Charlie made his way to the open-top buses. The first the others knew of the folly was when they heard a cry of "Come on you Spurs" and looked up to see Charlie at the front of the bus standing on a seat. Before anyone could get to him the drink kicked in and he wobbled, grasped for the safety bar, missed it and fell to earth with a horrible crunch. The fall left him properly monged for life but a nice touch came when Khan auctioned off a signed picture of Ian Dury sporting a Thistle scarf and donated the cash raised to help pay for a plaque at the museum. Khan even came up with a touching poem for the inscription. It read:

'Here fell Charlie Marriot,
He took his dram like a man,
Sorry you really are legless now
All the best from Amir Khan'

It is still there to this day as is the bond between Tottenham and one of Glasgow's less fashionable clubs. Fair play, Jags.

Back in the pub, Chariot led me out to the beer garden where I got my first sight of the Spurs Casual Spastics, and very impressed I was too. They were about to wheel to the Beehive, a pub sometimes used by visiting supporters, farther down Tottenham High Road where a spotter they'd borrowed from the able-bodied Tottenham crew (he just about qualified because of a bad ankle) had reported a gathering of their targets, the GIs. I was invited to join the 40 or so who were game and finished my drink just as the last wheelchair hit the fresh air, cheered on with those who were staying for more beer with "Give 'em some, lads" and chants of "S, S, SCS". I stayed at the back but could feel the sense of anticipation in the air as the SCS homed in on their prey. On the way, some foot soldiers of the able-bodied Spurs mob came out of the Corner Pin boozer near the ground and offered to push these wheelchair warriors to their meet. It almost went pair-shaped, though, when one plank queuing for chips from a kebab shop got the wrong end of the stick and pinched a bucket from the hardware store nearby and offered to help the lads raise some money. Wanker thought these boys were on some sort of charity wheelchair run. Chariot signalled to his second in command, Twisted Al, with a robotic, "Sort it". Al immediately dispatched the well-meaning knob with a wheel over the toes and a leather-gloved dig in the ribs. "S, S, SCS," came the call again, with Chariot following on about two minutes later with his electronic version. I joined in and we pushed the lads to about a hundred yards of the boozer. Then they wheeled themselves the rest of the way to the pub and Chariot's engine-powered chair was directed to the front door and, with a sudden surge of extra power, nudged open the door. There was a few seconds of silence. Then we all realised he hadn't quite managed to get the door open more than six inches. Someone standing near the door in the boozer peeked outside, saw Chariot and opened the door wide before asking: "Do you want to come, in mate?" A good two minutes later, and with 20 or so SCS waiting patiently in their wheelchairs for the possible 'off', Chariot's trusty voice box chip transcribed his painstakingly input instructions and sparked: "Come on then. Do you lot want it?" It lacked the inpact usually associated with this crucial point in a ruck and maybe the SCS should have elected another member to do this part, but Chariot was top boy and you couldn't take it away from him. No-one could. This was his moment. His life now. The buzz, the crack, the adrenaline. This was the moment it all kicked in. Chariot felt more alive at this moment than at any other time of his dreary, post-accident existence. For a minute, you could see he was lost in time. He was imagining he was up and about again, bouncing around, looking for the 'off' with the others, legging away fans along the High Road. Battering all-comers. Reality bites and it must have sharpened its teeth for Chariot as he electronically shouted: "Fuckin' come on" as he lurched back from his daydream and to the job in hand. With that there was a clamour to get out of the door from inside as a few game GIs tried to take up the offer. A few SCS at the back of the mob looked nervously at each other and one reached down to his wheels to escape the inevitable scrap but there was no getaway. Before any new SCS member can be accepted they must have brakes fitted to their wheelchairs to stop them going backwards. Clever stuff and it meant you could count on your numbers. In fact, the day you have your wheel lock removed is a big deal and a party is thrown for the new boy. It's a way of saying,'you've passed your initiation now, son. Welcome on board. Now get the beers in'. As the brakes locked in the first of the GIs managed to get out of the door and rammed into Chariot, sending him spinning backwards. It was then that it dawned on me how game this lad was...he couldn't move a muscle, for fuck's sake, and just moved his eyes with his head permanently lilting to one side. Yet here he was fronting up another mob. He was game all right. Twisted Al sped forward and nutted the pot-bellied Gooner and the sound of metal against metal filled the air as more GIs came out and went wheel-to-wheel with their enemy on derby day. At this point I saw a few of Tottenham's main firm (West Sussex Branch): Mark Newlands, Petworth Paul and Danny the Dagger. They were standing nearby applauding the efforts of the SCS and offering the odd blast of vocal encouragement. They'd brought some sandwiches and flasks of tea and were making it a really nice interlude before the serious matter of attacking their deadly rivals from N5 started a little later on. I know Danny quite well through my time on hospital radio voluntary work and actually interviewed him when I did a bit for Getwell FM, coming out of St Richard's Hospital, Chichester, for two hours every night. Danny and his wife Linda run a garden centre at nearby Goodwood and he gave us a really informed insight into the industry and chucked in a few green-fingered tips to boot. Top man. Those days might as well have been a million years ago now, though, as we watched these two groups of spazzos 'av it. Danny offered me one of his tuna sweetcorn sarnies and just as I bit in to the crusty bread a few GIs started to retreat to the safety of the pub only for their main paraplega-geezer to scream: "Sit, Arsenal sit" and they stayed put. The times I've heard the call go up, "Stand, stand. No one moves" during rucks but, of course, this was a wholly inappropriate choice of words when you're dealing with those confined to wheelchairs. Fair play.

Then, just as it was getting interesting, the familiar sounds of OB sirens screamed up the road and within minutes the place was clear. I just about managed to hand Danny my crusts and he packed the picnic hamper into the back of his VW Beetle before the OB started nicking a few strays. Twisted Al was pinched and was later fined £150 for his troubles. As usual, the boys chipped in and paid the fine. Nice one. We slipped away for what we hoped would be the real action to follow a little bit later on at the ground. The GIs had been game but took a beating yet they were unbowed. I heard later that one of their main faces, a nasty so-and-so by the name of Barrells, sent a letter of congratulations to the GIs for their efforts that day. It's nice when that happens. Despite the best efforts of north London's finest football hooligans, the afternoon passed quietly with the only action of any note came when the-then Spurs boss Christian Gross was given a dig by an irate home fan as he queued up to get the tube home later that night. Also, a few Gooners were surrounded in a pub up at Northumberland Park but after a 10-minute stand-off, all concerned decided it was far too cold and, much to the delight of the Boys in Blue, they decided to settle their issues with a darts match. For the record, Arsenal won, as they did the game 4-0. I caught up with Chariot just a few months before sitting down to put pen to paper for this book and he was in fine spirits but had to report that, sadly, wheelchair hoolie firms had dwindled considerably with the advent of special areas for them in grounds. "They have given us spastics credibility and dulled the ache to fight our foes," he told me over a pint in his local, the Fox's Neck. He still goes to the odd game at Tottenham but insists things aren't what they were. How true, my paralysed pal...how true.

Talking of things that aren't what they were brings me nicely on to the subject of sex. Nothing wrong with that I hear you say. And I agree wholeheartedly. What I can't abide though is sleazy sex...at football matches.

You see when it comes to a bit of the other, I'm straight down the middle. No questions about where I bat from, pal. I ain't got time for woofters, poofters, queers or queens. Disgusting. OK, there was a time in chokey when I watched a bit of bum-banditry in the next cell. But that's different, it don't make me a homo, does it? Homosapium, yes. We all are.

I was banged up with a proper hood, who went by the name of Enormous Andy, who ran with the Cobham Bonce-takers, a break-away faction of the more infamous Chelsea Headhunters. Story goes that Andy and his Cobham lot got the right hump with Chelsea's main firm one night after an inter-gang bridge tourna-ment at Wembley Arena left them out on their arse to an under-strength QPR outfit. Fair play. The Rangers lads had been hit by a flu virus and some of their top boys turned up under the weather and with pockets full of Beechams Powders. They doubled their doses and breezed it. The Rs had done their homework and on the night their "invitational bids" and "jump overcalls" were superb. Humiliation. Turns out some Headhunters with Andy, One-Eyebrow Babs, Big Bad Alex and Umbrella John, had been guzzling Stella and sniffing Charlie all night and they totally fucked up their "pre-emptive opening bids" while their "trump extractions" stunk the place out. Heated words were exchanged in the cloakroom and Enormous Andy started the ruck with a right-hander plum on the jaw of one of the Headhunters' top players, Talkative Pete. All hell broke loose with the Cobham lot immediately employing some cute bridge tactics of their own to outplay their pissed-up attackers. By the time the dust had settled, the cards picked up and coats collect-ed, the split was complete. To this day the OB have never known about one of the worst nights of Bridge hooliganism on record. Well they do now, mugs! You read it here first.

Anyway, more about Enormous Andy and my time inside later. What? You want to read more now. Well, sod you, I said later. Those who indulge in marmite-motorway shenanigans aside, the people who do get up my nose are those who seek their perverted sexual kicks shagging each other's wives...go by the name of swingers. Why so, I hear you ask? Ain't right is it. I mean, how do you know you are going to fancy the other bloke's bird for starters? And it ain't right that some of these planks have attached themselves to clubs. You come up against the likes of Doncaster Lay-by Doggers or

Port Vale Swap Posse and you'd be under no illusions that they can mix it. Yobs with knobs, they call 'em. Once the car keys are thrown in, it's every man for himself. We first had it big time with an inter-racial swinging mob over in the Isle of Wight one summer when me and the boys were pre-season camping. Back then pitching your tent a couple of weeks before the pre-season friendlies kicked off was common place. These days it seems laughable but in days gone by, before the advent of mobile phones, it gave you and your top boys chance to have a get-together, be at one with nature and relax before the season got under way. Shanklin on the Isle of Wight was our favourite spot but travel any of the more sedate and quaint sea-side resorts of England during this period and you'd find hoolies holidaying under the stars. AFC Sunderland's notorious Baden Powell Rokerites would hump their four-man tarpaulins to Whitley Bay (and more times often than not point-blank refuse to pay any-thing other than half the day rate for pitching); Norwich City's straw-sucking Carrow Soil Toilers could be found in Great Yarmouth while West Ham's Kent Coast Berrypickers were the only mob to go out on a limb and take caravans complete with awnings. Mostly to Southend. There were very few offs around this time. It was a time for reflection, chilling with your main men. Regaling each other with stories of battles and scraps. Real ale and plough-man's lunches and an evening of sing-alongs around a camp fire. Football songs, mostly. One time I made the mistake of bringing a snide Lacoste napsack along and never dreamt I'd be rumbled. Reddy, United's top boy at the time and one hell of a tent erector, sussed and went ballistic: "Show face at all times you little ponce," he snarled. "Snides are for mug campers. See that lot of ramblers, go walk with them if you think fake designer clobber is a giggle. Look at that bloke's fake Fila compass," he added pointing to some plum in bins checking orientation. "For fuck's sake, we've got a rep-utation to uphold."

I retired to my tent to consider what was one of the worst tellings off ever dished out in Shanklin. It was a bitter lesson, but a valuable one. To this day, all my gear is pucker. Back then I was a nobody on the ladder. These days I play by the rules. MY FUCKING RULES.

Pre-season camping was very much the calm before the storm. There would be plenty of time for trouble come the season. Trouble is, the rulebook was re-written, edited and re-written again when our idyllic camping area was invaded by the aforementioned inter-racial swingers over from Rotterdam in Holland and who had strong links to Feyenoord's feared Liberal-thinking Ultras. Feyenoord were due to play Pompey at Fratton Park and this bunch of nobodies were taking in some R 'n R just across the water from Fratton Park. Apparently, they were due to visit a Southsea sex club after the game. God knows what would have happened if Pompey's fearsome 7.02 mob (formerly 6.57, but brought up to date when the new Waterloo timetable came out) had known these clog-wearing muppets were within spitting distance. Bold as brass this firm of free-thinking fuckers had invaded our space, our terri-tory. Inadvertently admittedly, but we weren't having that. No group of Dutch bed-hoppers were going to fuck with us let alone fuck with themselves. It was a tricky one. How could we 'av it with this lot and at the same time show respect to the countryside and our fellow campers. You're bang on, dear reader...we couldn't. About 12 of us were deployed to the boozer they were supping their poxy Orangeboom and dotted ourselves all over. I was by the fruit machine and I could see this bearded Dutch twat necking with his black pal's white Doris. Blatant, it was. No respect. Come over to England openly flaunt your sexuality and you're going to get it, mate. Black or white. If these inter-racials wanted to act like domi-noes, they would have to fall like 'em, too. Big time. If there's no football, we'll find a reason to ruck. I used the public phone in the pub to call Reddy, who was back at the campsite waiting by the phone box. "It's gonna go any minute," I whispered, careful not to let the big-titter of a barmaid hear me. "They're at it in here, on our turf, Reddy. We ain't gonna 'av that." Reddy was quick to shout me down. "Shut it, you mug," he barked. "If you lot get stuck into them now, there'll be OB all over the manner within minutes. Wait for the signal." As per, Reddy was spot on. We were to wait until the Dutchies trooped back to the campsite and then confront them with "you're not swinging anymore" before steaming in. I thought it was clinched but Reddy pulled rank. Sure enough, the cheese-eaters drank up and, save for a last few bob on some takeaway cans, shipped out. They were 40 in number, give or take, and roughly even-stevens, birds and blokes. Never hit a woman, my old man used to tell me. Yeah but Dad, that was during the Second World War when you needed birds for the munitions factories. "Times have moved on, pop," I said under my breath. "These cock-hopping women are no strangers to an off." We tailed our prey back to the camp, making sure we kept enough distance to avoid arousing suspicion, tucking our bellbottoms in our socks to limit the noise of swaying jeans. The swingers started to jog gently, something was up...they'd twigged. As they approached the camp entrance, I heard the cry go up and Reddy, a former race course bookie, was looping his hand above his head to make the 33-1, double-carpet tic tac sign, the signal we were waiting for. "Here they are," came the shout. It went off big time with the Dutch standing their ground and going toe-to-toe with our top lads. I managed to deck a leggy black bird and then caught one on the chin from a blonde geezer with Cuban-heeled boots and a tight white vest. Then the familiar cacophony of OB car sirens filled the air. The Filth were here. We'd given it to them big time, as per, and most of us made it back to the safety of our tents. Reddy was captured and before the island's beak the next morning. The batty old bird of a magistrate mistook the whole episode as a tent-bragging scrap and ignored the OB's plea that it was related to football violence. Reddy had the nuts to thank this dappy Doris when she slapped him on the wrist with a £15 fine and the look and smirk he gave the OB when he breezed out of court was priceless. We never saw those Dutch swingers again but they did provide the launchpad for copycat English swingers to spring up. The rest, as they say, is history.

They may not rank as more bizarre than the swingers but one of the more unlikely groups of top boys to emerge over the past five years or so draws its members from Britain's nastiest bunch of bastards, traffic wardens.

Go by the name of The Perilous Yellow. That's right, traffic fuckin' wardens.

I can't abide these scum, nor can most people and that's why they felt the need to get up a firm of hoolies by way of protection. Since then they've attached themselves to various clubs, the latest of which is the Manchester Pistons basketball team.

Strange, right? Yeah, that's exactly what I thought. So did Stuart, the bloke I get my morning paper from.

But there's a bit of logic in this one. The football hooligan market is pretty much bloated these days while basketball is virgin territory. Or is was until those fuckers The Perilous Yellow latched on.

They bowl about in their all-black outfits and wear their peaked yellow and black hats around the wrong way when they are not on official duty but very much on unofficial business. The business of rucking.

I've seen them dish out beatings and witnessed them on the end of one or two, too.

One night coming out of Manchester Piccadilly en route to a Fall gig, I wandered into an almighty ruck. The Perilous Yellow had just had their post-Christmas Christmas party, something to do with it being cheaper after the festive period, something I've never liked. That's just tight. Ever heard of the festive spirit, boys? Thought not.

You should see the amount of detail and expense that goes into the Christmas do I organise for our lot. Proper Marks and Sparks crackers, strippers, the lot. More of that later.

So there they are, the infamous The Perilous Yellow, going toe-to-toe with what can only be described as a bunch of extras out of a Bruce Lee film.

(The Chinese king-fu master himself was a bit tasty and ran with Oxford United for a spell back in the Seventies after meeting their top man on the set of *Enter the Dragon*, which was being filmed near the Manor Ground.)

Turns out one or two of the more leery wardens had kicked off in Manchester's Chinatown. The Won-Ton soup had turned up tepid and they weren't having that, were they?

Bang, the table goes up, chopsticks are flung in the air and we've got a bloody riot on our hands.

The old Tiddlywinks are a close-knit group, though, and within minutes there are dozens of these slitty-eyed boys bouncing around, looking for the off.

The wardens were seriously outnumbered. Half of them had paid for an eat-all-you-can special for £7.99 (Monday and Thursday nights only) and stayed back to fill up. Extra noodles, any-one? Told you these boys were tight.

By the time I clapped eyes on the action, The Perilous Yellow were retreating...from ANOTHER perilous yellow...these Chinese boys.

They took a beating and since then I've heard they follow Arsenal ladies team and prefer Indian cuisine to Chinese. What, never heard of kebabs or pizzas, lads? Time you lot got out more.

I've had my own run-ins with these bunch of little Hitlers and smacked a few into the bargain.

Nowadays you need to be a bit cute when trying to negotiate the rescinding of a just-issued parking ticket.

Step out of line too much and clobber the twat and you may be in big trouble as their firm come marching around the corner.

I recently had to resort to minding my Ps and Qs when I got yet another ticket. Why so? The warden in question was Panther, their top man, and only son of the late, great comic Bob Monkhouse.

Panther knows the score only too well. Mutual respect, you might call it.

He knows I run with, lead even, a top, top mob. He does, too. We both do.

Panther didn't get his nickname because he had the speed of the big cat. No, that would be too obvious.

Or maybe he did because, come to think about it, he is pretty sharpish.

Anyway, the old sod couldn't believe his luck when he spotted my K-reg Mondeo parked on double yellows outside Safeways one Sunday afternoon in November a few years back.

I was in getting a rake of lager, 20 bottles of Grutnob German Lager, 5.5 per cent, to help me get through the afternoon's ironing. Yes, I am very much a look good, feel good merchant so ironing is important to me.

Just as I've loaded the beer into my boot, who should be staring at me from the bonnet?

Janet Spacey, a girl I went to school with. She was known as the school flea bag. She must have been de-loused because she was well worth a portion of my old love truncheon.

But next to her was Panther, with a great big fucking grin on his mush. Like a Cheshire cat who had got the cream.

And he had...me!

"Give it a rest Panther," I said, rolling my eyes to the skies.

"Don't mug me off."

Panther took some chewing gum from his gob and rolled it around his fingers. He was enjoying the moment, soaking up the fact that here he was getting one over on me, Aqua, top, top boy, and, let's face it, there was Jack shit I could do about it.

"Tell you what," Panther eventually snarled. "You give me them beers and we'll say no more about your little parking indiscretion. I've just got Billy Elliot out on DVD from Blockbusters so I could do with a few lagers when I sit in and watch it tonight. So, come on, hand 'em over,"

I weighed up his offer in a split second. The beer had cost me £12.99. The ticket was £40. It was money for old rope. I was now getting one over on him.

Job was a good one and fast-forward half an hour and I was in front of the box, feet up with some more lager and old fleebag Janet was doing my ironing. Quality.

We split up later that evening. I've never seen her since.

# CHAPTER TWELVE

# Diets, riots, Eye-ties and Tai Chi

AS football has progressed, not always for the best may I add, so too have things off the field of play. The obvious things are fashion, songs and the fact that more girls go to games these days. They are all very easy to spot. But one more subtle change has been the diets of the top firms.

When I first started to travel to football, first thing we'd do on a Saturday morning was all meet up at the local greasy spoon caff where we had the works.

Eggs, bacon, sausages, fried slice, the bloody lot, all swimming in grease, but by God it did the job. Brilliant stuff. It would be then onto the train, and get the ciggies and beers out for the journey. We'd perhaps take a wander down to the buffet car for a couple of pies or a sausage roll before jumping off the train and into the boozer for a proper drink before kick-off. A quick drop-in at the chippie near the ground, and that was it until the half-time pies.

Sink a few more pints after the game, then onto the off-licence to stock up for the return journey. Stellas at eight for a fiver, lovely. Once back in the Smoke, it was to the nearest boozer then an Indian or Chinese, sometimes both when we couldn't decide between us, before home, a nightcap, brandy or maybe a tot of whisky, and bed.

And that's the way all the firms ran things back then.

You see, all those years ago, none of us thought anything of it. One thing you just can't do is have a ruck on an empty stomach. It's like swimming after having a big meal or trying to chat a bit of skirt up after having a large doner with double garlic and chilli sauce. Mate, it ain't going to happen.

Things began to change a bit after Italia 90. Our clubs had been out of Europe for a few years after Heysel, and so for many lads the 1990 World Cup was their first taste of foreign travel. And for a lot of boys it was a real eye-opener. Sure, me and the lads I went with did get involved in a bit of the old you know what, but we also teamed up with a few Italian boys who were good enough to show us around. Two of the guys I remember were Antonio and Paulo, who were big Inter fans, and to be fair, they were as good as gold with us.

But the one thing that did cause a clash of cultures was Il Grubolino, or Il Noshino...food.

The Italian lads just couldn't believe what we English fans put down our necks. They tried, bless 'em, to turn us onto their Italian specialities such as pasta, sardines and risotto but as soon as our lot fancied something to eat it was either McDonalds, KFC or the nearest Turkish kebab shop.

I'll never forget the look on Antonio's face as we all sat down with a couple of bottles of Stella each and a KFC "bargaino buckettio", as they call them over there. He looked as if he'd come home and found us all in the kip with his Mama.

Antonio and Paulo asked how on earth could we fill ourselves with all that gear, then expect to go out and give a good account of ourselves on the terraces? They told us that the Italian Ultras had always been very careful about their diets and that some of the big firms even had their own dieticians who would travel with the crew, advising them when and where to eat before a big off.

They would only eat and drink organic stuff, regularly arrange spot checks at all their suppliers to make sure their meats were being correctly hung and the vineyards their favourite tipple came from were being run on the right lines. It struck us lads out there that these boys were streets ahead of us, and it made me determined to get things on the same footing over here.

Well, it's been a struggle I can tell you, but I must say over the last three or four years the English firms have at last taken dietary advice seriously.

When I first suggested to our lads that perhaps we could give the big fried breakfast a miss, and maybe start the day with a fat free croissant and a glass of Evian, well, let's just say their reaction wouldn't have been too different if I'd suggested missing the match and going to the Last Night of The Proms instead. Of course, lads will be lads and I took some serious stick from my mob for my attempts at cleaning up their food intake. I'd find chef's hats in my bag, mobile nutritionists would call at my house for an appointment made by one of the crew, you know, that sort of thing.

So, the great food revolution was put on hold. The away days remained a fat-fest, the home games an alcohol-fuddled six hours of junk food and more booze with nothing remembered the next day, the only clues of what had occurred were the curry and chilli sauce stains on your shirt and the terrible pain in the guts.

But things were about to change. A few seasons back, we drew non-league Notting Hill Town in the FA Cup third round at their place. These lads were Ryman League, but had progressed to mix it with the big boys via a string of decent giant-killing performances at Hull, Bury and Watford. To be honest, their team were just the normal bunch of journeymen ex-pros, brickies and builders, you know, the usual parade of lads loving their five minutes of fame before being propelled back into obscurity and midweek games at Welling, Aylesbury and Bishops Stortford. What did interest me was how, during the previous rounds, their firm had put up some very commendable shows against some not-too-shabby mobs and in particular the way they'd chased the Bury lads across the Pennines and up into Durham. Get you map out and have a look. Too right, that's a tidy run out.

Being Notting Hill, predictably their firm had more than its fair share of media-types with Jamie Oliver perhaps being the best known face. Some of you have probably seen the TV series Oliver did on Channel Four. "Hooligan Dinners" saw Jamie invited to spend some quality time with two firms, the newly formed West Ham Inter

Netty Firm, who are basically a web-based mob who only get involved in cyber-offs. They do go to games, but for the most part get their rocks off by downloading digital images of an off, compressing the file into a mpeg, emailing that to a blue tooth phone, then transferring that data onto an Ipod via a FireWire device, sending that information back to an Apple Mac mainframe, sending a stereo 3D version of that to a satellite phone then beaming it off into outer space. The idea doesn't float my boat but whatever gets you through the night and all that. The other lot were the Glasgow Rangers P.I.A. crew. It stands for the Pope Is Awful, apparently.

Anyway, Jamie and his TV crew stuck with these lads for a large chunk of the 2004/2005 season and the results formed the basis of "Hooligan Dinners". The first couple of episodes were basically our Jamie holding his hands up in dismay as he watched the lads in the firms demolish piles of pies, burgers, kebabs and chips whilst washing it down with enough booze to kill an elephant. A big elephant at that.

It was really enthralling to see how Mr Oliver attempted to persuade the boys to perhaps give the double jumbo burger and chips a miss and try the lightly grilled salmon with Chilean coriander and lime marinade with a couple of spoons of palenta on the side.

The one thing that did persuade the mobs that perhaps their diet needed an improvement was when one week Jamie brought over a tidy looking firm of top boys from Serie D side Valermo. Channel Four and the FA had arranged a three team tournament, involving Rangers, West Ham and Valermo with the games to be played at Upton Park over a weekend during the build up to the season. On the Friday night before the tournament, Jamie hosted a buffet/barbecue at his home at Notting Hill.

As soon as the Rangers and Hammers lads tipped up, they got straight onto the Stella, drinking it quicker then Jamie and his wife Jools could get it out of the fridge. The Glasgow boys then got stuck into some deep fried Mars Bars and Snickers before joining the Cockney lads on the assault on the burgers, sausages and meat pies. Meanwhile, the Italian mob sauntered in, popped open a few bottles of mineral water and downed a couple of olives each. Old Jamie couldn't get the burgers cooked quickly enough, and by 11pm the British boys looked about ready to explode. A few of them had already been sick in Jamie's pergola, and one of them had shat himself. Disgusting.

By this time the Italians had managed half a bottle of Frascati and half a bottle of Chianti between eight of them, and were picking at a plate of melon and raw artichoke. Their meal ended with a handful of oats, another glass of water and a couple of arias from a Verdi opera.

Predictably, the next morning, the contrast between the home-based firms and the Italians was there for all to see. The Valermo lads were up at 7am did an hour of Tai-Chi had a glass of warm water then set off for Upton Park. The West Ham and Rangers boys, at least those who could face it, set about a full fried breakfast and were back on the Stellas by 11am.

Before the first game, West Ham v Valermo, Jamie Oliver, a couple of white-coated dieticians from Whipps Cross hospital in Essex and that annoying little American bird from Channel Four's "You Are What You Eat" set up a mobile surgery next to the Bobby Moore stand and put the lads from each of the teams through their paces. After being weighed, having blood and urine tests, each lad had to produce a fresh turd which had been delivered that very morning. The dietician immediately went to work on the droppings, rooting around in them with a thermometer, a ph meter and various electrical probes. The results were truly staggering. Four of the British faeces seemed to have traces of some kind of radio-active material and had to be placed in lead lined boxes, sent by top security courier to Felixstowe where a coastguard launch was instructed, once it had made it into international waters, to throw the boxes overboard. This procedure was breaking every rule in the government's environmental policy document of 2001, but needs must.

The immediate area around the mobile surgery was roped off with yellow and black tape by the Metropolitan Police

You may know, you may not, it doesn't really matter I suppose,

**189**

that the average healthy male has a Fat and Toxins Rating (FTR) of 33.4. The results from these tests showed that the West Ham and Rangers mobs' FTR averaged 62 which was nearly twice the average. Bear in mind that a block of lard has a rating of 70, and you realise the state these lads were in.

Their urine was 16% alcohol, equivalent to a bottle of fortified wine, and their livers had been distorted to grotesque shapes and sizes.

Two of the Rangers mob were clinically dead.

Jamie Oliver simply stood outside the mobile surgery shaking his head chewing on an organically grown kohl rabi. In an emotive piece to camera, Oliver, close to tears, asked why these lads were filling their bodies with such rubbish, and why were we, as a society, letting all of our top mobs go to seed?

Behind him, the Rangers and West Ham lads are clearly seen queuing up at a burger van.

Oliver asked, just what would it take for these lads to change their ways?

The answer came a lot sooner than he, or anyone else expected.

During that tournament, the organically-fuelled Valermo firm put the British lads to the sword, big-style. The Hammers boys were chased across three counties whilst the Rangers mob only escaped a major beating by taking refuge in St Patrick's Church in Plaistow and claiming sanctuary.

There's no doubting that this was a definite watershed in the English hoolie world. Word soon got round to all the major firms that the time had come for our mobs to get their acts together and start looking long and hard at what they ate.

After the fall out from the Valermo drubbing, the ICF broke new ground on the English scene by advertising in The Lancet for a full-time dietician, eventually employing former Harley Street expert Dr William Green on £60k a year, with a company car and full BUPA cover. The Chelsea Headhunters continued the trend by bringing in Nigella Lawson and Keith Floyd to create their own brand of La Hunter de Tete organic ready meals for top boys to take to away games. Floyd was later relieved of his position after it was found the Cog Au Vin ready meal was in fact, just Vin.

As the look of the stadiums have changed over the last few years, it is noticeable that the once ubiquitous fish and chip shops, kebab and burger bars that traded on every street outside every ground are now all but gone.

Go to any stadium now, and around the home end before kick-off you'll find farmers markets, with dozens of stalls selling whole-some local produce, doing a roaring trade. Where once lads downed seven or eight pints of Stella, they sit and enjoy a Pain Rustic driz-zled with extra virgin olive oil. Lads' bodies are temples...and long may it continue.

Come to think of it, that little episode wasn't the only time that fine wine and good cuisine has played a significant part in my life following United. And, again, there was a big Italian influence. Although it was a very English telly cook who was at the helm of this one.

Most clubs have their celebrity fans, you know who I mean: Elton John at Watford, Birmingham have Jasper Carrot, Michael Grade at The Valley cheering on Charlton and Talksport's Mike Parry, an avid Evertonian. They watch the game from the director's box, munch on their prawn sandwiches and, you know, there is nothing wrong with that in my book. Most of them have put their hands in their pockets over the years to finance the club, so fair play to them if they want to sit amongst poncey businessmen in corpo-rate boxes. That's up to them. But not all of these celebs have always been rubbing shoulders with the great and the good. A number were once faces on the hooligan scene. As hard as it will be for you to believe this, dear reader, Delia Smith, who I mentioned earlier, for example, used to run with the Norwich firm the Canary Casuals.

I clearly remember a rather naughty visit to Carrow Road when we ran into Delia and some of her top lads. We arrived at Norwich on an early train from King's Cross, getting in some five hours before kick-off. We'd heard a whisper that Delia and her lads were holed up in a brasserie a few streets from the ground. We went from the station straight into the nearest boozer and sent a scout off to see if the home fans were indeed enjoying some pre-match nosebag. Ten minutes later our spotter returned confirming that their mob were necking a rather precocious but drinkable 1988 Beaujolais whilst awaiting their first course of truffles and wild mushrooms with Parmesan shavings.

A few of our boys were up for steaming in right away, but I decided it would be a better bet if we could get a few lads inside before it all kicked off. The plan was that me and Ashby de la Zouch Steve would get our feet under the table before signalling to our mob to pile in.

Steve and I trotted up the steps into the brasserie and asked the maitre de for a non-smoking table for two near the window. From where we sat we could clearly see Delia and her mob enjoying the tasty fungi and perusing the excellent wine list. I've always been a big fan of home made pasta, so I went for the linguine alle vongole, basically clams served on a bed of linguine in a white wine sauce. When this dish is done right, it really is superb, however I do remember an away day skirmish up at Newcastle in the mid 1980s, when the Toon had a decent firm, I was very disappointed with the way it was presented in an otherwise superb trattoria in Gateshead. I gave Steve a bit of stick as he went for rollatine di pesce spada, which are effectively swordfish rolls. Steve would always go for swordfish when it was on the menu, indeed his love of this particular dish had persuaded him to have the recipe tattooed on his back during one of pre-season away trips to Tuscany in 1995. We were in one of those four club tournaments along with AC Milan, Ajax and Athletico Madrid with the games being played at the San Siro over the last weekend in July. Our firm were holed up in the picturesque hill top village of San Guissopa and we'd drive into Milan for the games in a rented Fiat. One night Steve got mortal on the 1993 Chianti and awoke the next morning with the full recipe, in Italian of course, illustrated on his back. But I digress.

So, there we were at the table enjoying the first course when we were clocked by one of the wine waiters. He sauntered over to us with our Frascati, bottle of sparkling water and some warm home baked olive and walnut ciabatta.

We got talking and it transpired his name was Ultra Giovanni, and surprise, surprise he was one of Juventus's top boys. His eyes lit up when we told him we had a mob outside who were all ready to have a pop at Delia and her firm.

He let me know that he and the sous-chef, a Lazio face who had once deliberately served the Roma coach his fillet steak rare when the bloke had ordered it medium rare, we well up for it. What a quality piss-take! These boys were more than ready to help us sort them out. Apparently, only the week before one of Delia's boys had sent a plate of mussels back complaining they were cold and another had criticised the Soave, reckoning it was corked. Giovanni let it be known that he and his mate were more than happy to help us out with a bit of payback.

As it turned out, we didn't need the help of our newly acquired Eye-tie pals. Delia was a cute so-and-so and had spotted us come in and make friends with the staff. Before we could lob a few wine glasses in her direction to provoke her and her mob into an off, the wine waiter bowled up with a Veuve Clicquot La Grande Dame, which has got to be £100 a pop. What could we do? How rude would it have been to try to kick Delia and her boys up and down the High Street after the gesture she had just made. The bubbly was opened and poured and, with the first sip, I raised my glass to Delia's table, bit like you see in the mafia movies when they show each other the utmost respect. We ended up sinking another bottle and by the time we got back to our lot, the impetus had passed. And one or two of the senior lads has copped the hump for us. We didn't care, though. We were full of top quality fizz after all.

As well as dietary needs for the lads it's funny how the game has changed over the last ten years or so – due to the formation of The Premiership, Sky money blah blah blah. I mean look at the players these days. Not too long ago you'd look at your squad at the beginning of the season and there'd be a couple of Sweaties, maybe a

Paddy or a Taff, perhaps a couple of Mancs, and the rest would be local lads who had come up through the youth set-up.

Every chance you'd know a few of the lads from school. Hey, don't get me wrong, I'm not on about travelling to the game on the bus with the centre-forward, I might not be in my first flush of youth, but I ain't a pensioner, either!

No, what I mean is you'd have a connection with the team. You'd feel that the lads out on the pitch were representing you and your town. And I suppose, in a way, we felt the same when we were having it toe to toe on the terraces. We were sticking up for our town, we were stopping a bunch of northern sheep shaggers from taking liberties on our manor, or we were doing missionary work in the uncivilised outposts of out great kingdom by turning up at some smelly, grimy shit hole, and showing their boys just how to take a home end.

But these days when you look at the first team squad, and even the youth set-up, these lads come from all over the gaff. At first it was France, Italy and Spain – now they come from all over. Once it was names like Zola, Cantona and Vieria, basically think of a name and stick an A on the end.

But now it's Lua-Lua, Boa Morte. Fair play to these lads, back in their homeland they were probably poverty-stricken. The scout for Arsenal tips up, hands over a wad of money and the next minute this fella is living in a penthouse in St Johns Wood and driving around in a Merc.

It must be one hell of a change of culture for these fellas and it's no wonder some of them go mental, and get on the beer. One minute they're living in the heart of Africa, the next they're at Spearmint Rhinos up west with a Page Three stunner on their arm, two bottles of Moet down their neck and a couple of large in the wallet.

And you do wonder what goes through their heads when the team coach pulls up at places like Turf Moor and Millmoor on a wet Tuesday night. Don't forget, these poor beggars have never had the benefit of watching Coronation Street or my old mate Fred Dibner blow up them chimneys. They just can't be ready for a tour round

Middelsbrough or Barnsley. Think I'd prefer living Africa come to think of it.

It's not only the players who have changed. All the top managers and coaches are now foreign. Wenger, Mourinhio, Benitez. They're all over here managing our teams.

But surely this is just a fad, a fashion. I just don't understand why the clubs feel it's a good idea to go abroad and bring some garlic-cruncher or spaghetti-eater over to run the team. It's just a case of keeping up with the Joneses, you've got a frog in charge so we'll have an eye-tie. But it won't last forever. Sooner or later the foreigners will pack up their berets, pasta, clogs and paella and piss off back to where they came from.

Oh yeah, I can already hear the woolly liberals getting all hot under the collar about what I think. Reckoning I'm some kind of BNP right wing nutter who goes round dressed up as a Nazi stormtrooper and thinks Rudolph Hess was a top boy.

So, I'm sorry to disappoint you when I tell you there's nothing I like more than six pints of Cobra or Kingfisher and a night in the Taj Mahal. Even the taxi driver who drives me home is one of that crowd. That's blown your argument right out of the water, I'm afraid.

Thing is, and don't get me wrong, I'm not pretending I'm the first one to come up with this theory. But we, and I mean us lot in the UK, we're not connected to anyone. Apart from the Sweaties and Taffs, but there's not a lot we can do about that. That bloke Hadrian had the right idea if you ask me, but that's another story.

You see, the French, the Germans, Italians and all that mob...well, basically it's one big country, mainland Europe. Half the time you don't know whether you're in Belgium or Holland or France. Apart from a sudden outbreak of lederhosen or clog-dancing, you wouldn't have a clue where you were.

And it's been like that for centuries, since the Ice Age or whatever, and that's why they, the foreigners, will always stick together against the English. It's in their genes.

They probably can't help it, even if they wanted to. It's like their languages. You can't tell me that basically, all their lingo isn't the same. Their stuff is more or less everything we say but with an "i" or an "a" on the end. Apart from the Germans. Enough said.

Take UEFA for instance. Now if you go to watch your team away in Europe, you're likely to have bags of piss thrown at you, flares and rockets fired at you, their OB have been twitching with antici-pation since the draw was made and have spent the time polishing the batons and servicing the water cannons. During the game the home fans will spend the entire 90 minutes trying to get at you, whilst the OB and what they laughingly call stewards over there, stand by and watch it all happen. You'll be spat on, crapped on, you'll have seats thrown at you, you'll be stopped from having a beer and a sing-song then locked in for two hours after the game has finished, frog-marched to your hotel, then shoved on the first plane home. And if, just if, you stand up for your rights, the OB will take great delight in giving you a right hammering with the previ-ously mentioned batons. Then, when you do stagger off the plane at Gatwick or Heathrow, swathed in bandages and black and blue, the press and the TV cameras will be there ready to denounce you as a disgrace to your country.

Yet, in the return leg, if an English fan even farts UEFA want us thrown out of the competition, our ground closed, all English clubs banned from Europe again. You know the routine.

That's because UEFA is based in Switzerland or somewhere and not fucking Stoke. Fact!

All the European football big knobs sit around having long lunches, drinking their wine and eating frogs legs and keeping it all nice and cosy. They'll chat away in foreign about Milan, Barcelona and Ajax and not give our clubs the time of day.

And what do our FA do about it? Well, FA is about right.

No, now that I've given it some more thought, we're an island race with an island mentality and thank fuck for that. If it was down to me I'd brick up the Channel tunnel tomorrow. Pull out of the EC and shut down all them poncey coffee bars that have cropped up in everyone's high street.

We're English and we drink fucking TEA.

# CHAPTER THIRTEEN

# Still well up for it!

MOBILE phones, the internet, satellite navigation systems, inter-continental ballistic missiles. Years ago none of these existed let alone played a major part in having it with a bunch of Geordies or Taffs. These days they are the tools of the trade when it comes to football hooliganism. Apart from the inter-continental ballistic missiles. They have no part in today's hooligan warfare. Although some of the hardcore Stoke firm would be first in the queue should they ever go on general sale. But you don't have to go too far back to find a time when a Stanley knife, a party six and a lot of front were the only must-haves on the day of the match. Oh yes, Planet Yobbery has a far different landscape in the 21$^{st}$ Century than it did during what many describe as the halcyon days, the 70s and 80s. Being well up for it these days means you need to be on the cutting edge of technology. Once upon a time simply showing up at some tin-pot outpost with a bunch of game lads and tracking down the home mob was a simple process. Front up their main boozer early doors and they'd soon come calling. Now lads plan scraps weeks, months and sometimes years in advance with mobile phones and the net their chosen forms of communication. One firm especially keen on ultra-planning is the Munich 1860 boys over in Germany. They have a top boy who works for the Kraut FA and he has a big say in compiling the fixtures so can pretty much tell the firm who and when they will be playing years in advance if necessary. None of the suits at the Bundesliga have a Scooby Doo that this lad runs with the Munich mob, although on several occasions in the past some of the Bayern firm have threatened to spill the beans. This has resulted in a peace-pact between the two rivals and now the bigger club from across the city can actually request two fixtures to be sorted to suit them. It's not something we in England go into too much, being best buddies sort of defeats the object, but these two get on famously and are even planning to share a stadium after the World Cup 2006 so I hear. Ground-sharing? Can't see United and City doing that can you? OK, maybe those days aren't that far off given the regular City-United fundraisers over the past few years. But, nah, can't see it. Your enemy is your enemy is your enemy. United and City sharing a ground? Can't have that. Yes, it's a fact of life that hooliganism has moved on at an alarming pace but it does-n't suit everyone. A lot of the younger hoods in our firm have embraced it and we leave them to it. OK, it's necessary but doesn't mean I have to get involved to any great degree. I'll leave some of the youth to text some lout in Liverpool to fix a ruck or email some Herbert from Halifax to arrange an off. And I'm not alone in shying away from the age of the cyber-scrap. I am very much a tradition-alist when it comes to beating the living crap out of someone, tak-ing the piss out of the OB or simply burning down a boozer before a game. Yeah, I miss the old days. Who doesn't? Mob sizes are nowhere near the numbers the top firms could boast back in the day. It wasn't unusual for us to assemble up to 4,000 boys for the key battles of the season. These days what is recognised as a decent turnout can number anything from between 50 and 300. But I move on. I accept my lot. I embrace just about enough of the new ideas, new methods, as I have to. Truth be told I still hanker after the days when everyone knew the score except the bleedin' OB. The rozzers were normally the last ones to know we were in town and taking great pleasure in smashing it to bits. But I won't be taking it as far as some lads. An interesting innovation over the last few years has been the rise of the tribute firms. Basically, these are gangs of lads acting out rows that occurred years and years ago. Think of the Sealed Knot Society, then go and do one. Funny, right? A joke, yeah? No, mate, deadly bleedin' serious. They love it, this lit-

tle lot. I've travelled with these boys and really do admire their ded-
ication and eye for detail. These lads have the lot: silk scarves,
rosettes, crombie overcoats, tonic trousers, ox-blood Dr Marten
boots. The works. OK, they stop shy of taking a rattle to the games
but then what lagered-up lunatic would get very far wading into the
oppo with a red and white rattler?

Fair play to them, I say. They take it deadly serious, poring over
newspaper cuttings from mostly the 70s getting each and every
detail right. They mimic these yobs in every way, shape and form.
They don the right clothes, have the correct haircuts, speak the
same language and it even goes right down to the drinks and cigarettes they smoke. Some would say they take things too far. I say,
again, fair play. One bunch, The Busby Boys, obviously Manchester
United lads, are so into it they actually believe they are still in 1969
and only use pre-decimal money. The money thing does cause problems, as you can probably imagine. After all, not too many turnstile
operators these days accept threepenny bits and half crowns
(except the Scousers). So, a lot of the time, these lads don't even get
into the ground to see the game although there are a few enterpris-
ing locals who set up currency exchange booths opposite the
grounds which United visit. A few boys get in with the help of the
United players, who often help out with a few comps. Phil, before he
moved to Everton, and Gary Neville are well aware of these boys
and will always do what they can to make sure as many as possible
get in. The brothers collect all the spares from the squad about half-
an-hour before kick-off and then send one of the physios out to dish
'em out. I'm told Sir Alex Ferguson even helps out when he can and
his wife Cathy knows the lads and is always chatting to them about
their "costumes" before the games she attends.

They're the terrace boy equivalent of the Amish. Getting in is
one problem and getting to the games used to be another. Again
money was the main problem with countless train ticket collectors
shaking their heads in disbelief when they were confronted with a
ticketless mob offering a ten bob note as payment. What these
United lads did next was ingenious and downright crazy into the

bargain. How they ever pulled it off I'll never know for sure, but pull it off they did. With the help of some investment bankers who were Old Trafford regulars with a soft spot for their cause, they managed to get enough funds together to buy their very own train. The Busby Boys' top lad had learned of a transport museum in York which had one too many decommissioned InterCity trains and was looking to either offload it or use if for parts. "Love'n'hate" Declan, you guessed it, his nickname came from the tattoos, although for some strange reason they are on his toes, managed to persuade the museum curator that a 1967 train back in working order and running football fans up and down the country was a good idea and so the project was born.

The Manc lads spent every spare second fixing up this old rattler. Anyone who had ever lifted a spanner, ever wielded a paint brush in anger, was put to task. Two years of hard graft paid off and The Pride of Salford was ready. There was to be an unofficial unveiling with very much a low-key approach. All the lads, the bloke from the transport museum and the Neville brothers' dad, Neville, had agreed to break a bottle of bubbly over the old girl to launch her back onto the country's railways. But, as so often is the case with these things, the press got wind of the event and, in turn, local politicians and dignitaries, liasing with the Manchester Evening News, made sure they snaffled some of the invites which had been dished out to the bods at York museum. Trouble was, as was so evident to Declan and most of the top boys, the city's great and the good were in for a big surprise when the giant canvas sheet was finally removed from the first carriage and the fizz duly cracked open. For the train hadn't exactly been restored to, er, let us say, its former glory. Although in a sense, and in the eyes of the restorers, it had, you will discover. By the time of the unveiling the Busby Boys had managed to persuade the then Minister of Transport, Edwina Curry, to grant special permission for the train to run the length and breadth of our railway system. And with her help in obtaining a lottery grant aimed at protecting our heritage, the lads even managed to bulk buy all the discarded place names from the mainline stations. The plan was for one of the boys to make the journey the day before and place the original signs over the modern ones so as to make the trip even more authentic when the train pulled in. I'm not sure it ever happened and you'll probably find, if you dig a bit deeper, that the lottery money was supped in the various boozers dotted around Old Trafford. I really don't know, couldn't possibly comment if I did, although I bumped into some of the boys at a recent England game at Old Trafford and, well, let's just say I never put my hand in my pocket once and slept through the game pie-eyed. Cheers, lads. And Browny you mad bastard, stay off the vodka-Red Bull cider-tops! Anyway, the day of the unveiling came and you can imagine the look of horror on all the bigwigs' faces when The Pride of Salford was revealed complete with 70s style graffiti, ripped seats, broken windows and piss-stains on the seats. The lads wanted authentic and they were determined to have it right down to the last detail. There were gasps from the assembled audience, the press scurried away to write about the "shame of lottery funded louts" and Declan and the boys went down the pub for a good drink. Cheers, Edwina.

Tell you what, though time certainly flies – and that's a fact. Yes, it only seems like yesterday when I was a fresh-faced kid travelling to away games with the top boys, running errands for them, shining their shoes, soaping their backs during overnight stays at some roadside hotel, listening in awe to their stories, and getting my first taste of the knuckle, the grunt.

Well, now I'm one of the lads the new youth get the beers for, I'm one of the top tidy mob who tell the young 'uns how it was back in the 70s and 80s, as I've explained. Ipod? I remember that Cec Podd who used to play for Bradford. But that's about it.

It's funny, but although tons of things have changed since I first started going to football – I mean who, as I've pointed out, thirty odd years ago would have dreamt about mobile phones, for instance? – only that bloke Steve Nokia who ran with the Forest mob pre-Cloughie, I suppose. Blimey, that geezer must have made a packet – him and that Dr. Marten, quids in.

Yeah, although many things have changed, a lot's still the same. You know, you and your crew turn up at say The Reebok, Pride Park, Madjeski, The JJB and it's all new and clean – shopping malls, cinemas, DIY stores – oh look, there's the football ground.

But the thing that keeps football going, is people like me and you. You, who are reading this book. Unless you are OB or NCIS that is. Write your own bloody book, boys. Or go and shine your truncheons.

Better still, go down to your local library and check out a book already written on your side of the story by the former head of the Met football intelligence unit, Commander Terry Scott. Won't take you long to read it and realise it's tosh from top to bottom, though. Would have been more authoritative if 70s actor Terry Scott had written it, for Christ's sake. Scott gets it all wrong. Every page reveals exactly why the OB are fighting a losing battle against the likes of us, the boys, even in this day and age. In one chapter, laughably entitled *Divide and rule: Curtailing Unlawful Activity by Fair Means or Foul*, Scott tells how he managed to divert a nasty bunch of Wrexham's finest boys from a pre-arranged off with QPR's firm on Shepherd's Bush Green by nabbing them at Euston and shepherding them on to a Tube train and into the ground three hours before the game, thus missing their allotted timeslot for a row with Rangers. That's complete hogwash, Scotty, and you know it. As is quite common for the Wrexham lot, they had sent their infamous decoy mob on the train to the smoke that day, made up mainly of retired lads and youth who were still learning their trade. The main firm, as is often the way with the Welsh boys, came in by bus and made perfect timing for their off. One of the Racecourse rowdies' tops boys, Crazy Les, puts the record straight in his book, *Wrecks 'Em: Frontline Crew, the Untold Story*. It reads: "August 28, 1996: QPR away. The decoy boys did our 'bird' for us in the stands at Loftus Road while we made the trip on the National Express for £12.99 return. The OB nabbed them at Euston and they were in the away end by noon. Fine by us. That's what a decoy mob is all about and we still can't quite believe more mobs don't go in for this tactic.

Works every time, look. Got to the green and had a few liveners in the alehouse before meeting up and having it toe-to-toe with QPR. No casualties apart from Big Jonesy who lost his lapel badge and broke a zip. Saw the top OB after the game and he nearly choked on his radio when we told him about the decoy situation." That's what it says, Tel. Explain that one. Still, made you a few quid for your retirement fund, I suppose.

Yep it's all about us, not the poncey suits who are sitting in their executive boxes eating their steak and chips and watching the game behind glass, with one eye on the racing from Chepstow, one on the arse of the pretty little thing who's topping up their wine glass – and the other on the game. Yeah, OK, that's three eyes – but I hope you get my gist. Roy Keane got it right when he called this lot the Prawn Sandwich Brigade. Make that Prawn Baguette if you're over the Arsenal, eh Roy? By the way, good luck with the house move (me and Roy go back a long way but that's another story).

Dear old Roy got it bang on this time. It's the fans like us who really matter. We cough up the dough for a season ticket, and spend hours travelling all over the country in trains, hired vans, motors and scooters (especially in the case on the Port Vale Parkers, a section of the Burslem boys who combine watching their team with re-runs of Quadrophenia and Who gigs). When we arrive at an away ground, we don't get a plate of prawn sandwiches and a glass of something in the boardroom – no, all we get is the OB pushing us around like cattle and the local hoolies running around trying to have a pop at us. We're then shoved into the most Godforsaken part of the ground, either up in the Gods, miles away from the action on the pitch, or we're left to freeze our nadgers off on an open terrace. Try standing for a couple of hours on the away end at Oldham on a January night – you'll soon see what I'm on about. Fair play, though the Bovril and pies are exceptional at Boundary Park, it has to be said.

The point I'm making is that it's fans like us who make the club tick. We are the club. We'll be travelling up to 'Boro or down to

Plymouth whether our club are top of the Premiership or about to fall into the Conference. We'll be there after the manager, chairman and players have long gone. In some cases we'll be there when we are dead if we choose to have our ashes scattered on the hallowed turf. We've seen them come, and we've seen them go.

But what thanks do we get? If you do ever get the opportunity to bump into one of the directors or coaching staff, with a very few exceptions, they treat people like us as cannon fodder. The badge-kissing players, well let's face it, most of them don't know what fucking city they're in. They've had a couple of years in Italy and Spain, and now it's our turn to finance their penchant for sports cars and yachts. Rolex watches and endless Bling. They'll say the right things, get paid a king's ransom – get caught with their trousers down in a local crack house or whore house, and move on. And so it goes on.

As for the suits, they have no idea about supporting a team. To them, we're a bit of an embarrassment. If they're honest about it, they'd prefer it if we just went away and left them to it. Left them to turn our game into some kind of Disney-themed day out for the nuclear families with their 2.4 kids. A mixture of baseball and Billy Smart's circus. Their idea is for us all to arrive at noon, have a bar-becue in the car-park, then ooh and aah at some geezer with a flare strapped to his leg parachute onto the centre-circle. We'd all then watch the game, applaud politely at the right moments, go home quietly and be back next week for more. Well, I've got a bit of bad news for these characters. You see, it's not their game, it's our game. The lads' game.

We're the lads who have a few beers, make a bit of a racket, and maybe have a ruck now and then. We are, and this is the kind of language they use, "dragging the club's name through the mud" – or we're "stopping the 'real' fans and families from coming to the game". These Johnny-come-lately mugs have the audacity to ques-tion the loyalty of lads like us. To them, football is entertainment – nothing more, nothing less. What did the Yanks at Budweiser call it in a recent TV ad campaign? Soccertainment! Ain't far from the truth though and how long before that Malcolm Glazer character who owns Manchester United starts to try to change things to give our game the stars'n'stripes-style glamour and glitz? Not long, I bet. To them, it's just another distraction. It's like going to the cinema, going out for a spot of supper, going to the opera – I don't know what these characters do of an evening.

And as they've shelled out a few grand to have some kind of influence on what goes on, they see it as their duty to rid the club and the game of working class oiks like us. Ain't happening, pal. Not now, not ever. They want to gentrify the game, make it more accessible to the middle-classes, to families, to women – make going to football the same as a day out at Alton Towers or a night at Glynbourne.

These suits love the idea of inviting their no-chinned Tory mates to the game for a glass of bubbly and a plate of nouvelle cuisine before watching "their" team take on the Mancs or the Chels. Arse is more appropriate.

Oh yeah, they'll bang on about how fantastic the centre-forward from the Ivory Coast is, or how well the Italian goalkeeper has adapted to the Premiership. But if you ever get the opportunity to collar one of these characters, ask them who the manager was in 1979 – forget that, ask them who the manager was in 1999 – they will not have a clue.

Ask them where they were at The Vetch in '84 when 300 fucking mad Welshmen did the windows on the coaches, or where they were when those Spanish tossers were waiting for us at Madrid station that night when we played Athletico? Probably sitting in Daddy's debenture seats at Twickenham watching the Varsity Match or maybe down in SW19 watching yet another failed campaign for British tennis stars at Wimbledon. Wimbledon? Try Plough fucking Lane on a miserable, wind-swept January evening watching the reserves because a first-team player is playing in a comeback match after a long spell out with a fucked knee. Not now, obviously, because they play in Milton Keynes. That's a joke as well but don't get me started on that one.

Ask them, these cigar-chomping, Windsor-knot tie-wearing wankers, exactly what it feels like trying to get to sleep on Barnsley station on a February night after the FA Cup replay went to penalties and there were no trains back to London until 6am. And you lost. Ask them what it feels like to wake up in Leeds Infirmary surrounded by the OB after being hit on the back of the head by a half brick lobbed into the way end by one of Yorkshire's favourite sons. Try running out of oxygen half way up Mount Putha Hiunchuli en route to seeing a pre-season altitude-training match against Nepal Bigfoots! (August 1977, seeing as you ask, and no, we didn't make the match but it cost us a £300 each for the pleasure).

Oh yeah, we're the scum of the earth we are. We're a cancer on the game. A blight. A carbuncle. A bloody nuisance. The prices rise and rise and still we come. We'd sell our grandmother to pay for a season-ticket. Not mine, because she has passed away, bless her soul. You lot, you snooty bastards, you just right it off on expenses. Try real work. Try grafting in a factory for £250 for a 39-hour week and having to do a car boot bright and early Sunday morning to flog off the kids clothes to raise a few quid. Clothes they have grown out of, obviously. Fuck me, we're not that bad.

Yeah, well, we'll see. Let's see who's still here in five years shall we?

When the bubble's burst, when the money's run out, when football is no longer the new black. When the Bling has been blown. When the czar of Chelski has taken his billions elsewhere once he has become bored with his new plaything at Stamford Bridge.

Let's see who's bringing their boys to the game, paying through the nose for cheap, shit kits sewn together in some back street sweat shop in Bangkok, putting up with the whims and ridiculous pontificating of the latest egomaniac who has, with the assistance of various dodgy financial skullduggery, somehow managed to assume control of a club.

Lads like you and me won't have moved on to rugby or Formula One or kangaroo boxing. We won't have left the club with our tails between our legs, bored with our latest toy.

No, we'll be there, watching our team, supporting our club. Business as usual.

Still well up for it.